WINDOW OF GERANIUMS IN HOME OF MR. & MRS. M. H. ARNDT

The five tall pink flower clusters in the center are of 'Tobey.' Three large red flowers at their left are 'Fiat Queen.' Half a cluster of 'Peaches and Cream' shows at the lower left, with the larger, deeper rose flowers of 'Patricia Audette' beside it. Three plants of 'Wicked Lady' with enormous rich dark wine-red flowers occupy the fore part of the front row. These are all forms of *Pelargonium hortorum*. The *domesticum* hybrid, 'Orchid Edith North' shows directly beneath 'Tobey.' To the right are the two large, bright pink clusters of 'Fiat Enchantress,' a *hortorum* variety. To the right of these, but in the front row, is another *domesticum*, 'Rose Marie.' Two ivy geraniums, 'Jeanne d'Arc,' and 'Souvenir de Charles Turner' (the most pendent one), hang over the edge of the window box. Other forms of *P. hortorum* shown are the colored leaved and red flower clusters of 'Miss Burdett Coutts,' the ivory-bordered foliage of 'French Lace' on erect, almost vinelike stems, and silhouetted against it, the large red cluster of 'Fiat Supreme,' and a red cluster of 'Ostergruss' against the wall.

GERANIUMS
FOR HOME AND GARDEN

HELEN K. KRAUSS

New York
THE MACMILLAN COMPANY

To my granddaughters

KATHRYN LEE and BRENDA ANNE

PREFACE

The "old-fashioned" geranium has become a new-fashioned plant. It has never been completely out of style, for no group of plants possessing so reliably the qualities of sturdiness, variety, and beauty could lose caste among appreciative gardeners. Its popularity, however, has waxed and waned, and now it is again on the increase.

Development of a wider range of flower and foliage colors has stimulated some of the new interest in garden geraniums. Flowers and foliage of all types are being increasingly used in bouquets, arrangements, and corsages. Growers are also responding to the attractiveness of ivy geraniums, the appeal of the scented-leaved kinds, the ornamental quality of the florist's type of pelargonium, and the uniqueness of the deciduous sorts with their curiously fleshy stems.

This awareness has brought about the formation of a new International Geranium Society, which, it is hoped, will further promote knowledge about this highly favored group of plants. (P.O. Box 231, Santa Paula, California.)

The former peak of popularity for geraniums (or, botanically speaking, pelargoniums) occurred in the early 1800's. During the intervening years, when only a few kinds were being grown, much of the early information about these plants was lost, except to those who were willing to spend their time in libraries and to seek out living plants which had been long in cultivation. A dominating purpose of this book, therefore, has been to search the literature and to study living plants in order to clarify the history and identification of the many kinds of pelargonium at present being grown. Of the 760 different kinds that are treated in this book, about 99 per cent are in cultivation in the United States today. There are, in fact, many more than this being grown, for new variants are being created at a rapid pace by both amateur and commercial growers.

On the other hand, of the several hundred kinds developed by hybridization and selection, mainly in England, nearly 150 years ago, relatively few are known today. Some, however, are still outstanding; others are occasionally seen. To determine which of these have actually survived has been like running down the clues of a detective story.

In searching for the original names of pelargoniums being grown in America, all available European botanical literature has been examined. Recourse was had to European and American periodicals and trade catalogues. California trade catalogues and lists from 1914 to 1935 were available to the author in incomplete pamphlet form; it is to this California period after World War I that most of the undated *P. domesticum* hybrids mentioned in this book are ascribed. Frequently hybrids were grown in European countries and in America for ten years or more before they were recorded in literature. A similar situation applies to several imported pelargoniums which have not been traced to their source; in this circumstance the date of introduction into America is given.

In a group as widely hybridized as *Pelargonium*, no list of names of plants known in cultivation can ever be complete or completely free from error. There are disastrous pitfalls as well as valid reasons for this inadequacy.

Without formal registration, names are bound to be duplicated. Also, closely similar forms of plants are given different names by different growers. It falls to the lot of the compiler to segregate such conflicting information. Reliance must be placed in part on the published literature, including catalogues of past and present; in part on one's personal experience in growing many kinds and in studying the collections of other growers.

There are times when a decision on which name to include for which form must be somewhat arbitrary, but in the present volume a conscientious effort has been made to avoid both types of duplication mentioned. Some favorite names will therefore be found missing; but to include every name known in the trade would have made this volume unwieldy for both mind and hand.

Therefore, for each group of cultivars (horticultural varieties), only a selection of named kinds has been provided. These are meant to comprise not a definitive list of everything ever named, but a helpful guide to the grower, either amateur or professional, to desirable forms that are in the main available in the American trade.

To reduce the synonymy with any degree of certainty the growing habits of more than seven hundred pelargoniums have been studied; a few species were observed growing in their wild state near Cape-town, South Africa; a collection of native species was observed at the National Botanic Gardens in Kirstenbosch, South Africa; other species were studied at Kew Gardens, England; and numerous species and early hybrids were examined at The New York Botanical Garden.

After their historical and botanical background is given in Part I, four major groups of pelargoniums are covered in this book. First in Part II there are the garden geraniums—the familiar bedding, window box and window plants, to which the group name of *Pelargonium hortorum* has been given. Among these are the dwarf types, also those with colored leaves. Of similar cultural requirements, but less known, are the attractive ivy-leaved geraniums, *Pelargonium peltatum*, considered as the second group. Those that florists recognize as "pelargoniums" come third, and they include the showy "Lady Washington" geraniums; to the botanist they are known as *P. domesticum*. Fourth is a varied group with markedly scented leaves containing numerous species and hybrids.

In addition, there are many interesting pelargoniums of unique characteristics. Some of these are succulent-stemmed desert plants; some grow fleshy tubers; many are deciduous and in culture, therefore, require a long resting period. These, with some of the parental species of present-day hybrids, are treated in the closing chapter of Part II. Part III deals with pelargonium culture.

While the cultivation of most pelargoniums is a relatively simple matter and does not strain the skill of the experienced gardener, basic principles of plant growing must be understood if success is to be assured. Climatic conditions in America differ from those in Europe and the methods of handling pelargoniums vary also. In this book we shall attempt to present accurately, if somewhat briefly, information on the growing of pelargoniums in the window garden and sunroom as well as in greenhouses and out-of-doors.

Many notable persons—horticulturists, botanists, and librarians—have contributed their knowledge and scholarly resources toward the making of this book. To each and every one, including those whose names remain unknown to me, I am deeply indebted.

My gratitude is first expressed to Mr. T. H. Everett, Horticulturist of The New York Botanical Garden, for making available his card index of references to Pelargonium and Geranium in the Garden's library; also for the loan of a collection of herbarium specimens.

Many others have cheerfully gone to great trouble to locate and freely place at my disposal rare publications on Pelargonium. Among these are the librarians Miss Elizabeth C. Hall of The New York Botanical Garden, Mrs. Ruth A. Duncan of the American Philosophical Society, Mr. William T. Stearn, Librarian of The Royal Horticultural Society in London, and Miss Marion Code of the Pennsylvania Horticultural Society; also Mr. Arthur Cornelis, who obtained for study the privately owned collection of all volumes published by the Vick nursery firm of Rochester, New York, from 1861 to 1890.

For valuable assistance on critical details of the manuscript, my respect and thanks are due to Dr. Harold E. Moore, Jr., of the Bailey Hortorium, Ithaca, New York; Dr. Donald E. Munnecke, Plant Pathologist at the University of California, Los Angeles; and Mr. Paul W. Jackson, then Executive Secretary of the International Geranium Society, Santa Paula, California, among others.

If the name of Milton H. Arndt seems to appear in this book with undue frequency, it is because I am so greatly indebted to him as friend and neighbor while I have been toiling on the manuscript. Among the almost countless different kinds of pelargoniums he has grown, Mr. Arndt has successfully developed hundreds of new hybrids. I fully recognize that in other parts of the country, less accessible to me except on occasional travels, other growers are producing fine plants which are also taking an important place in American horticulture. These have been included whenever I have had personal experience with the individual varieties.

Thanks are tendered to The American Philosophical Society for reproductions of photographs from early Pelargonium literature, and to Mr. Arndt for many of the other photographs shown in this book. I am particularly grateful to Miss Mildred Capron for her photograph of geraniums (pelargoniums) growing wild in a valley of the Twelve Apostle Mountains in South Africa, where we enjoyed some adventurous treks together.

H.K.K.

CONTENTS

Contents

Illustrations are between pages 82 and 83.

PART I

Introduction

Chapter I

GERANIUMS THE WORLD OVER

Around the globe few groups of cultivated plants can approach the universal popularity of geraniums. These gaudy, sturdy plants from South Africa are cherished in nearly every country of the world. Exuberant with bloom, they burst from windows of Bavarian cottages and Swiss chalets, and they seem to spill from rocky heights on the Riviera. They are familiar sights on country window sills throughout North America. Their leaves and flowers accent symmetrical designs in Dutch and Belgian dooryard plantings and make ribbons of color in England's public parks.

The doors of Irish cottages are flanked with gay geraniums, and the living-rooms of Scandinavian and Russian homes are brightened with their blooms. In Peru and Mexico they clamber like vines against sun-drenched walls. In Portugal the plants spread from gardens to the neighboring mountainsides. Seeding themselves from nearby yards, they have invaded southern Italy's farmlands. In Asiatic gardens they lend an exotic note which may inflict nostalgia upon a lonely visitor from the Occident.

Indoors and outdoors everywhere, geraniums have been grown with pride and affection for more than 200 years. Whether the plant is spoken of by its familiar name or given its technical designation of *Pelargonium*, it is as frequently admired growing unpretentiously in a sunny window in New England as in a dramatically designed garden in California.

3

The hardy wild geraniums of North America and Europe are quite different, though they are related plants. The botanical genus *Pelargonium* is one of several distinctive groups in the Geranium family, of which the genus *Geranium*, with wild species in the northern hemisphere and other temperate climes, also is a member.

Nearly all of the several thousand different kinds of pelargoniums grown in America and elsewhere are descended from the wild species of South Africa. Here the evenings are cool and the long days are brilliant with sunshine throughout the growing and flowering season. South Africa is a land of bush, rather than of towering trees, so regardless of whether the native plants grow at sea level, on mountainside, or mountain top, very little shade is available to them. Though the winters are cold and rainy, they are rarely freezing. Since very little rain falls during the summer months, most parts of the land assume a semiarid condition before the season's end. The evenings, however, are cool enough to offset the daytime heat. Thus the South African native geraniums—pelargoniums, that is—are enabled to reach a maximum in size.

In climates approaching that of South Africa, as in parts of California, where they can live outdoors the year around, geraniums also attain great stature. In such places they frequently seed themselves, often to faraway countrysides, where these emigrants will spring up among the native plants as though they had always belonged there.

Specimens cultivated in the colder parts of North America, where the season is limited, are more usually kept to moderate size. Although it is possible to grow specimens to four feet tall or even more, in order to house them in their winter quarters it may be necessary to prune them down to a convenient size after their outdoor growing season. In regions of continuous heat, such as southern Florida, the geranium does not flourish unless given special care.

Where they do grow well, geraniums are being increasingly used as cut flowers. Within the past few years they have become more and more popular for bridal party bouquets. Double flowers are preferred to single ones, as they do not shatter so readily; however, the shattering may be obviated by putting a drop of florist's glue in the center of each individual flower.

I have seen bridesmaids' bouquets composed of the delicate pink flowers of *P. hortorum* 'Mme. Jaulin,' soft salmon-pink flowers of 'Mrs. Lawrence,' and the more vivid salmon-pink flowers of 'Mme. Landry.' At a St. Patrick's Day wedding, green-ribboned bouquets made up of white flowers of 'Mme. Buchner' were noted. There are numerous varieties of garden geraniums with long-stemmed flowers that are now being used for flower arrangements at flower shows as well as for decorative purposes in the home.

THE GROUPS OF GERANIUMS

Since the eighteenth century, four major groups within the genus *Pelargonium* have been cultivated. These are the so-called garden geranium (*Pelargonium hortorum*), the ivy geranium (*P. peltatum*), the kind most often called pelargonium by gardeners (*P. domesticum*), and the scented-leaved pelargoniums of numerous species, hybrids, and cultivated forms. Though the popularity of each has risen and fallen from time to time, the ebb has fortunately never been extremely low. Otherwise we would not be growing today the hundreds of favorites that were developed from fifty to one hundred and fifty years ago. These early pelargoniums are still as handsome as many of later origin.

The Garden Geranium

The most familiar kind of all is the garden geranium, for its nearly globular clusters of bloom in red, salmon, pink, or white and its roundish scalloped leaves have been seen in outdoor beds and indoor window gardens for many generations. Of complex hybrid origin, the group has been given the name of *P. hortorum* (see Chapter 1 of Part II).

There are subdivisions of the garden geranium that are quite different from the type, even though their ancestry is essentially the same. One of these comprises a group of dwarf forms usually sought by collectors who desire plants that require little space. Some of these are miniature replicas of their larger sisters; 'Tiny Pat' is one of them. Dwarf forms grow slowly but develop into bushy mounds covered with small leaves. When in bloom certain of them look almost ludicrous, their flower clusters are so large. These little plants are excellent for edging of flower borders as they stay within bounds without needing to be pruned.

There are also fancy-flowered sorts which are equally floriferous and just as easily grown. No collection, indoors or outdoors, is complete without one or more of these specimens. To choose from are types with flowers that resemble miniature rosebuds, cactus-flowered kinds with quilled petals, "bird's-egg" flowers in which the petals are heavily peppered with dots, and "picotee" types with flowers of toothed petals resembling those of carnations.

Another subdivision consists of plants with colored leaves, and these are again divided according to the leaf colors. The most highly prized are the tricolors, most of which have actually more than three colors in an individual leaf, A remarkable thing about these plants is that a few of them have been perpetuated for almost a hundred years. 'Miss Burdett Coutts,' for example, which shimmers in silvery tones and brilliant hues, still rates as one of the handsomest in its class after close to a century of culture. However, most of the plants of recent origin have more brilliantly colored leaves than those of the earlier era. These include 'Skies of Italy,' with pointed-lobed leaves that suggest scintillating stars, and the rounder-leaved 'Carlton Velma.' These plants produce fine clusters of colorful flowers, but the leaves in themselves are so ornamental that adding flowers is like the proverbial gilding of the lily.

Ivy-Leaved Trailers

The trailing geraniums with shining green ivylike leaves (botanically known as *P. peltatum*) are members of another important and handsome group of pelargoniums that grow as easily as the garden geranium either outdoors or in the house (see Chapter 2 of Part II). It is an enchanting sight to see the flowering branches cascade from a window box or over a garden wall. Although the flowers differ somewhat in form and marking from those of *P. hortorum*, they are equally colorful and showy.

Domesticum Pelargoniums

The group of geraniums which gardeners have habitually called by its proper name of pelargonium (*P. domesticum*) consists of a vast number of variants bred from many ancestors of different growing habits (see Chapter 3 of Part II). This mingled heritage may account for cultural requirements that differ from those of the two preceding groups.

In the East these plants are generally grown by nurserymen who are equipped to provide them with the low night temperature necessary to bring them into flower indoors about March. 'Edith North' with its gay flowers of salmon-pink is a popular kind grown for the Easter trade.

P. domesticum is more popular on the West Coast, for there the many different kinds can be grown in the open ground throughout the year. They are also favored as potted specimens for the patio or terrace. These plants furnish cut-flowers for corsages which arouse the admiration of visitors to California.

Scented-Leaved Types

A vast array of different forms is present in the leaves of the scented-leaved pelargoniums, which are largely known for their pungent, often flowery scents (see Chapter 4 of Part II). They comprise a large group of easily grown plants that respond gratefully to the simplest attentions of the gardener. Many scented-leaved geraniums were grown in English and Scottish herb gardens long ago, and no modern herb garden is complete without some of them. Only by comparison are the flowers less significant than those of the garden geranium. The foliage in itself enjoys the distinction of being ornamental whether on a growing plant or used in a flower arrangement.

Commercially, several species or hybrids of the scented-leaved pelargoniums are cultivated from southern France to Turkey and in Kenya Colony, Africa, for their roselike oil. This is used as a substitute for the more expensive attar of roses extracted from rose petals for the manufacture of perfumes. The most important crops consist of *P. graveolens* or derivatives from it. To a lesser extent *P. radens, P. odoratissimum* and *P. fragrans* may be grown. *Pelargonium capitatum* is frequently listed as an important commercial plant but it is not certain that this species is in use. Names given to the oil-producing plants are not to be trusted, and this one has been confused with a hybrid of *P. graveolens*.

Rare and Unusual Plants

In addition to the pelargoniums of the four major groups already discussed, there are numerous ancestral species and related pelargoniums, as well as unique plants of odd habits which in this book are grouped together for convenience under "Rare and Unusual Pelargoniums" (see Chapter 5 of Part II). Among these the following are especially easy to grow: *P. praemorsum*, with small leaves that suggest fluttering butterflies and many sprays of airy yellow flowers; *P. reniforme*, with a compact mound of small velvety leaves, and flowers that grow on and on like those of a vine; *P. cordifolium*, with lilaclike leaves and distinctive flower clusters.

P. echinatum and its relative, *P. stapletonii*, are not difficult to grow, and they produce clusters of handsome flowers, but their deciduous habit leaves the stalks bare and unattractive during their resting period.

Other pelargoniums, such as the black-flowered *P. ardens* and other tuberous-rooted kinds, and those with gnarled or gouty-looking stems, are prized by collectors who understand their special requirements. These plants are usually grown only in private greenhouses and in botanical gardens.

Chapter 2

HOUSE-PLANT GERANIUMS FOR BEGINNERS

Fortunately for the beginner, the great majority of geraniums are easy to grow indoors. From the four major groups described in the previous chapter, there are several hundred kinds from which one may choose with satisfaction for culture in the house. Given a fairly heavy soil and a sunny spot, they will thrive with little care other than watering. (For specific cultural directions, see Part III.)

By making selections from each of the groups that are mentioned below, the uninitiated grower will be enabled to appreciate the many variations which exist in the genus *Pelargonium*. These cultivars * have been chosen in order to provide diversity in foliage, scent, and flower form and color.

Among the garden geraniums (*P. hortorum*) there is a wide color range to choose from in both flowers and foliage, and many are not as well known as they should be. Tinted pink kinds include the variety 'Berthe de Presilly'; pink with salmon tints are 'Fiat' and 'Irvington Beauty'; apricot-salmon, 'Mme. Landry.' Among the reds a bright soft tone is found in 'Hall Caine'; scarlet in 'Helen Michell' and 'Paul Crampel'; and light crimson with white center in 'Dryden,' which is an exceptionally good winter bloomer. A crimson one is called 'American Beauty'; purples include 'Suzanne,' with handsome dark-

* The word "cultivar," used today where gardeners formerly used the word "variety" to refer to a horticultural form, is explained in Chapter 4.

zoned leaves, and 'Monsieur Emile David.' The most popular white kind is 'Marguerite de Layre.'

Among the *P. hortorum* cultivars there are also numerous sorts with brightly colored leaves that add gaiety and variety when flowers are absent for a time. None of the following are difficult to grow in a window garden. Popular kinds with colored leaves are 'Skies of Italy' and 'Carlton Velma.' 'Mountain of Snow' and 'Mme. Salleron' have variegated green or silvery green and white leaves. A charming member of the group is 'Distinction' with crinkled bright green leaves that are narrowly zoned with black-green near the edge.

Because of the vinelike habit of ivy-leaved pelargoniums—those of the *P. peltatum* group—pinching back of new growth is often necessary to keep them under control. Pinching need not be done, however, if the plants are placed on pedestals or elevated sufficiently to permit the stems to droop naturally so that they are free to fling out their colorful flower clusters. Within this group there are some shorter-stemmed ones too. Those especially recommended are 'Galilee,' and two with vividly colored flowers, 'Charles Monselet' and 'César Franck.' Another ivy geranium to be considered is 'Cordens Glory' with few, short, lax branches and brilliant flowers; this is a vigorous plant that looks more like a garden geranium in habit and leaf.

Forms of *P. domesticum* are generally not as reliable as the others when grown under average house conditions. 'Earliana,' however, is easy to handle, and 'Mme. Layal,' with its pansylike flowers, is popular for indoor culture. Both are conveniently small in stature.

From the scented-leaved group, fragrance and diversity of leaf shape have been the criteria for the selections mentioned here. *P. crispum* with small crisped leaves, is lemon-scented; *P. graveolens* with larger leaves, deeply divided, is rose-scented; *P. odoratissimum*, having scalloped and rounded foliage, is sweet-apple scented; *P. tomentosum* with broad, downy, coarsely lobed leaves is mint-scented. 'Concolor Lace' has a mild foliar fragrance. Its low, bushy, spreading habit adds to its other qualities, such as the light green lacy appearance of the leaves, to make it a desirable house plant. All of these have been favorite subjects in window gardens for more than a century.

Chapter 3

GERANIUMS FOR BEDDING

It was a pleasing sight one day to see a bed of orange and apricot-orange geraniums set against the dark brick background of a New Jersey house. At the seashore not far away I saw window boxes planted with faintly orchid, pink tinted, and lavender-pink geraniums which combined beautifully with the flowers of hydrangeas growing below them. Such colors and combinations are all too seldom seen. Others available but infrequently used include purple of different degrees of intensity, old rose, peach-pink, white and rose-pink in combination, and white alone. There is no reason for confining our choice to the scarlet, crimson, and salmon-pink varieties when so many others are available. Yet, outside of California, parts of Mexico, and in private gardens in other parts of America, only about a dozen varieties of garden geraniums (*P. hortorum*) are popularly grown for bedding purposes.

Equally useful and even more showy for bedding is *P. domesticum*, the pelargonium of gardeners. The flower clusters and individual flowers too are larger than those of the hortorum group. Few of the flowers are monotoned, and many are multicolored. These sturdy, erect, and attractive pelargoniums will thrive in any part of America where the evenings are cool. (The outdoor culture of all the different types is described in Part III.)

Vinelike pelargoniums are grown for different purposes in different regions of the world. In California, *P. peltatum* is used to some extent as ground covers. The tendency of these plants to creep along on flat surfaces makes them worthy of a place in border plantings; they are easily controlled to conform to the area allotted to them. In many parts of Latin America, *Pelargonium peltatum* is used with striking effect to cover walls. The flower clusters are numerous and showy, rising above the foliage, and flowers are produced throughout the summer and fall. The range of flower colors within this group is sufficiently large to permit a selection of analogous or contrasting shades to grow with pelargoniums of other groups.

Scented-leaved geraniums with distinctive growing habits may be sought for the border. Low bushy kinds include *P. odoratissimum* and its derivatives, *P. fragrans* in several aromas, and *P. graveolens* 'Lady Plymouth.' Those which grow tall and erect are eminently suitable for background planting. Among these *P. denticulatum* and *P. radens* are recommended for their fernlike foliage and liberal branching habit. The *P. quercifolium* derivative, 'Fair Ellen,' grows about to the height of average garden geraniums; it is worthy of consideration because of its bushy habit, handsome flowers and dark green oaklike leaves. Larger geraniums with spreading lax branches are also useful; should the branches grow out of bounds, judicious pruning is advised and the branches can be used advantageously with cut flowers of any kind. The fragrance of scented-leaved pelargoniums in the border is a constant delight to all who casually brush by or tread on a leaf which has strayed out of bounds.

Pleasing effects can be attained by planting garden geraniums with variegated green and white leaves such as 'Flower of Spring' or 'Mrs. Parker.' Lower growing kinds, which would be attractive in the border of the flower bed include 'Mountain of Snow' and 'Wilhelm Langgluth.' Low bushy pelargoniums with highly colored leaves also make excellent border plants; those recommended for growing in full sun are 'Skies of Italy,' 'Carlton Velma,' and 'Maximilian.'

Garden geraniums are occasionally grown in tree form (generally known as standards). The procedure for growing is quite simple, but it requires patience and watchfulness as it may take a year or more to produce a tall specimen with a bushy head. Only vigorous and tall growing plants should be selected for this purpose. All shoots should be removed right from the cutting stage, and only one or at most two stems should be kept. These should be made to grow on as rapidly as possible until the desired height is attained. Then the head is allowed to develop. Further pinching of the branches that compose the head is necessary for yet more branches to form so that the head will be dense and productive of more flowers.

Among the hundreds of cultivars of *P. hortorum* adapted for growing into tree geraniums, the following are suggested for their flower colors: 'Alexian Beauty,' 'Radio Red,' 'Masures Beauty,' 'Maxime Kovalevski,' 'Mrs. E. G. Hill,' 'Barbara Hope,' 'Dryden' and 'Marguerite de Layre.'

Several tall and vigorous geraniums with colored leaves are also now available for developing into tree form. These are of rather recent introduction and are distinct from all other *P. hortorum* cultivars having colored foliage. The leaves are large and their soft hues blend or contrast harmoniously with the large clusters of flowers.

Whether colorful plants are wanted for edging, background, filler, solid bedding, or striking specimens, there are satisfactory geraniums to fill the need.

Chapter 4

CHARACTERISTICS

The geraniums (pelargoniums) in cultivation are mostly perennial plants with persistent stems of a somewhat woody nature. While the majority of them have fibrous roots, about eighty tuberous-rooted kinds are recognized by scientists and of these about a dozen are known to horticulturists. The tubers are usually large, often turnip- or potato-shaped. Tuberous-rooted pelargoniums are deciduous, shedding their leaves generally after they have flowered. At this time they require a resting period of two to three months, whereas the other types can be kept growing the year around as long as conditions are favorable.

STEM STRUCTURE

Stems are usually succulent in new growth, becoming woody as they mature. In different species and varieties they may be green, brown, or almost black; smooth or hairy; very slender and hairy as in *P. fragrans* or very slender and smooth brown as in *P. praemorsum*. The species *P. carnosum* and *P. alternans* are among those having very thick brown or black stems which are enlarged and knotted at the nodes, giving somewhat the gnarled appearance of Japanese dwarf trees. Green stems with swollen nodes are characteristic of *P. gibbosum* among others. *P. tetragonum* is unique in having green, fleshy, square—sometimes triangular—stems. A few kinds have no visible stem above the ground.

14

LEAVES OF VARIED FASHION

Each leaf consists of a blade and its petiole, or leaf-stalk. At the base of the petiole, where it joins the stem, there is usually a pair of stipules, often somewhat thin and papery in character. *P. echinatum* and its derivative *P. stapletonii* have stipules which in age suggest the spines of cacti. The arrangement of the leaves along the stem is mostly alternate, but occasionally opposite; or they may arise in clusters from the crowns of stemless sorts, or from the tips of stems and branches as in *P. apiifolium* and *P. quercifolium* 'Pretty Polly.'

Pelargonium leaves assume a great variety of shapes and sizes. The simpler forms may be ovate (egg-shaped), cordate (heart-shaped), reniform (kidney-shaped), lanceolate (lance-shaped), palmate (like the fingers and palm of a hand), peltate (shield-shaped and attached to the petiole near the center of the blade), deltoid (triangular) or cuneate (wedge-shaped). The margins may be entire (smooth-edged) to bluntly toothed, crenate (scalloped), incised (deeply cut), or variously lobed to different depths. Lobes may be again divided, often into threes, sharply angled, wedge-shaped, or rounded. Flat surfaces are abundant, but waved and ruffled margins are also frequent within the genus.

The more distinctive leaf forms are those which are finely divided. These may be variously described as pinnatifid (with the segments cut almost but not quite all the way to the midrib), pinnate (feathery, like a feather of a bird), or bipinnate (twice divided; that is, when the primary divisions are again pinnate). The divisions in the leaves of pelargoniums vary from a sixteenth of an inch or less in width, as in the feathery *P. abrotanifolium* and *P. rapaceum*, to a half inch or more as in *P. quercifolium*. The latter has pinnatifid leaves; *P. pinnatum* has pinnate leaves; *P. fulgidum* and *P. apiifolium*, bipinnate leaves. Both pinnate and bipinnate leaves are sometimes evident in 'Concolor Lace.'

Perhaps the most unique leaf patterns among pelargoniums are those of symmetrical geometric designs which resemble architectural drawings. Among these are *P. graveolens*, *P. denticulatum*, and *P. fulgidum*.

The texture of leaves varies from thin as in *P. praemorsum* to thick and succulent as in *P. peltatum*. *P. inquinans* has soft velvetlike leaves and this character has been transmitted to many forms of *P. hortorum*.

P. fragrans and *P. odoratissimum* leaves are as softly silky as short-piled velvet; the leaves of *P. zonale* and many of its descendants sometimes suggest a coarser velvet; *P. tomentosum* leaves are like plush or soft felt; *P. quercifolium* harsh, while *P. denticulatum* foliage is sticky on the upper surface.

Leaf colors range from gray green through light to very dark green. Metallic purple areas through the center of dark green leaves are peculiar to *P. quercifolium* and its derivatives. Leaves of *P. zonale* and many of its offspring are noted for a dark horseshoe-like zone; *P. frutetorum* and certain plants of *P. peltatum* origin also have zones, but these are of different shape and size. Others have variegated leaves of green and white or green and creamy yellow. Highly colored leaves with silvery white, yellow, orange, rose red, and red are characteristic of one of the subdivisions of *P. hortorum*.

FOLIAR FRAGRANCE

Scent is not exclusively confined to the scented-leaved group, as must be evident to those who handle and grow the garden geranium and certain varieties of *Pelargonium domesticum*. Rose-geranium oil used in the manufacture of perfume is derived primarily from *P. grave-olens* and a hybrid. The lemon-scented *P. crispum* has been a favored plant in gardens for more than two hundred years. Other scents include the apple-like fragrance of *P. odoratissimum*; the mint scent of *P. tomentosum*; the pungency of *P. quercifolium*; and numerous other spicy and aromatic odors of which *P. fragrans* provides a notable example.

FLOWERS AND THEIR PARTS

The flowers of *Pelargonium* are borne in an umbrella-shaped cluster or inflorescence called an umbel, in which all the individual flower-stalks arise from the same point at the end of the short or long peduncle (the main stalk that supports the flower cluster). These umbels may be few-flowered as in *P. radens* or many-flowered as in some types of *P. hortorum* where the cluster may attain a diameter of six inches or more. Occasionally, as in *P. praemorsum*, they have only one or two flowers. Most often the umbels are borne singly and opposite or sometimes in the axils of the leaves along the upper part of the stem. *P. reniforme,* however, produces an inflorescence of numerous umbels branching from a single stem that sometimes rambles to a length of two feet. *P. cordifolium, P. cucullatum* and *P. tomentosum* are examples of pelargoniums that produce umbels in a branched inflorescence somewhat like a panicle.

Each flower is supported by a small stalk called a pedicel that varies in thickness or length according to the type of pelargonium; the shorter the pedicels, the denser or more crowded the flower cluster appears to be; conversely, when the pedicels are long and slender, the flower cluster assumes an airier or more open appearance. Dense flower clusters may be noted in *P. graveolens,* the hairiness of the pedicels and sepals of this species adding to the appearance of density.

The Spur

Another character affecting the appearance of the flower is the spur, or nectar tube. This appears as a slender tube extending downward from the uppermost sepal and attached to the pedicel. A careful investigation will show that the lower end of the spur is marked by a swelling, which looks merely like a little bump on the pedicel. The spur can be seen more easily by slicing the flower lengthwise with a razor blade between the two upper petals. It will then appear as a slender, hollow tube on the upper side of the flower stalk.

In Part II, the spur will be mentioned again, particularly in Chapter 5, for pelargoniums may often be divided into groups depending on whether the spur is long or short. Long-spurred species have a spur two to three or more times as long as the sepals, a familiar example being *P. hortorum.* Here the spur is often so long that one has to look at the very base of the stalk to see where it ends. Short-spurred pelargoniums, on the other hand, have a stubby spur that is generally less than one and one-half times as long as the sepals. *Pelargonium domesticum* and most of the scented-leaved species are examples.

Petal Shapes and Colorings

Flower colors in the species range through red, purple, lavender, pink, salmon, and yellow to white; and many of these are ornamented with either dark or bright colored spots and markings on the upper petals. *P. quercifolium* and the derived 'Fair Ellen' are examples of plants with dark spots. Dendritic marks (like miniature trunk and branches of a tree) are common in many species, such as in *P. hispidum* and in many derivatives of *P. peltatum*. Brightly colored veins, streaks, or stripes are abundant throughout the genus. The combination of unrelated colors in individual flowers is a special character of *P. domesticum* varieties, often with large dark spots in the upper petals.

Although flower petals in the species are usually irregular with the two upper petals broader than the three lower ones, length and breadth vary in different pelargoniums. The petals of *P. pinnatum* are long and narrow; those of *P. crispum*, *P. echinatum*, and *P. quercifolium* are broad and showy. Within the *P. hortorum* group are many with rounded and overlapping petals. These are a deviation from the species in that the petals are nearly equal in length and width. Deeply fringed petals are characteristic of *P. bowkeri*; toothed petals occur largely within the *P. hortorum* and *P. peltatum* groups. Narrow, twisted, rolled, or curled petals also are found largely within the *P. hortorum* group.

Reproductive Organs

Insignificant so far as the flower's appearance is concerned, but of fundamental importance in the perpetuation of the genus, are the reproductive organs. As in *Geranium*, the flower of *Pelargonium* normally contains ten stamens, but in *Pelargonium* some are merely threadlike filaments, functionless in that they lack anthers to bear the pollen, which is the male element of the flower.

The slender pistil in the center of each bloom narrows into a column, called the style, which spreads into five minute branches or stigmas, at its tip. The ovary at the base is divided into five vertical compartments, known as cells or carpels, each of which may bear one seed. When ripe, the outside walls of these carpels split along their seams, and the seed is carried upward and outward in a curve by the spiral twisting of the stylar portion, which is often beautifully plumed. Before the seeds blow or fall away, a ripened seed vessel often has a decorative form, something like a miniature chandelier.

Chapter 5

NOMENCLATURE

Those animate and inanimate things which man wishes to distinguish one from the other are given names. An apple is an apple and not a peach. Mary is Mary and not Margaret.

Is an apple or a peach the same as a rose? Each one represents a different genus within the Rose family, the Rosaceae. So it is with *Geranium* and *Pelargonium*: each one represents a distinct genus within the family Geraniaceae.

When a geranium is spoken of, eastern gardeners will generally visualize the eastern *Geranium maculatum* with lavender flowers, while others may have in mind one of the western species that grow in or near the woodlands of other parts of the United States. Some may think of similar kinds imported from other regions of the world to be grown in our semishaded gardens. Others think of another kind of geranium, botanically known as *Pelargonium*.

The major differences between *Geranium* and *Pelargonium* are:

1—The flowers of *Geranium* are regular, that is, they have five similar petals; the flowers of *Pelargonium* are irregular in that the two upper petals are alike and usually broader than the three lower ones.

2—*Geranium* (except in the mountains of some tropical regions) is a herbaceous plant, that is, it dies to the ground each year; *Pelargonium*, with few exceptions, is a subshrub with a more or less woody stem.

3—Numerous species of the genus *Geranium* are hardy; with only one known exception, members of the genus *Pelargonium* cannot stand freezing temperatures outdoors in the climate of northern United States.

4—In *Pelargonium*, each flower has a nectary within a tubular spur which extends downward from the calyx and is attached to the pedicel, quite unlike spurs of such plants as the columbine. This distinctive character is not always obvious to the untrained observer, yet the form of this spur may become a determining factor in identification of the different species.

Thus a pelargonium is a pelargonium for very definite reasons. But, as there are perhaps thousands of kinds of pelargoniums known to botany and horticulture, and these differ from each other in form, color, habit, or other characteristics, it is necessary to distinguish among them and apply to each a distinctive name. It is sometimes said that names are not important, yet people commonly invent and apply names when the correct ones are not known.

To know a true name and the reason for it is to increase one's pleasure in an object. A plant in the garden whose name can be spoken assumes a character denied to those which are nonentities.

KINDS OF NAMES

Each pelargonium has only one correct technical name. This does not preclude the possibility of a pelargonium having more than one name; it may and often does, in addition to its technical name, have one or more vernacular names and these vary in different parts of the country and in different parts of the world. We have no quarrel with folksy names as such, provided they do not cause unnecessary difficulties in identification. But one must remember that such names may not convey to others the meaning we wish; only by employing the correct technical name can we hope to distinguish with certainty the plants we talk and write about.

To illustrate, the name "rose-scented pelargonium" seems distinctive, yet it is confusing and often misleading, for it is applied to several species and hybrids, some of the latter being almost devoid of rose scent. It does not belong to any one kind exclusively; consequently, if a person refers to his "rose-scented pelargonium" we may not know, without actually seeing a specimen, to which particular pelargonium reference is made.

The classification of plants and the system now used for naming them has evolved over a period of centuries. In ancient Greece the importance of naming plants correctly was recognized and the difficulties inherent in proper classification were realized. Through the ages physicians were obliged to know the plants they employed medicinally, and herbalists needed to know the plants they grew and prepared for physicians. Their names, however, generally included several qualifying adjectives.

Carolus Linnaeus, the Swedish "father of modern botany," coordinated all the usable knowledge of the past and reduced the complicated names to two simple words—a noun and a distinguishing adjective. These names he offered to the scientific world in his volume called *Species Plantarum* in 1753. Two centuries later, still following Linnaeus' simple system, technical names are governed by rules that have been developed over the intervening years and are now formally recognized by botanists and horticulturists throughout the world.

In order to make the present book as modern as possible, the suggestions offered by the International Code of Nomenclature for Cultivated Plants have been used. This code was adopted by the Thirteenth International Horticultural Congress held in London, England, in 1952, and was published by The Royal Horticultural Society in 1953. The more important provisions of this code are explained in following paragraphs.

The first of the two words used by Linnaeus, the noun, is called the generic name. It is a broad designation, such as *Pelargonium,* and is spelled with a capital letter. When the second or qualifying name, the adjective, is added, the specific name is formed. *Pelargonium scabrum,* for example, is the name of a species, or of one particular kind of plant, within the genus *Pelargonium.* In present-day nomenclature, the tendency is to spell all specific names with small letters, and this practice is followed in this book.

Sometimes species are found to vary from the type in definite patterns. When this occurs among plants, especially in the wild, botanists add a third, or varietal, name to the designation. Thus *Pelargonium scabrum* variety *balsameum* is a balsam-scented variety of *P. scabrum* with more finely divided leaves. The use of italics indicates that it is a botanical name.

HORTICULTURAL NAMES

Horticultural variants, with which we are chiefly concerned here, are called "cultivars" instead of varieties. These are also given names but they are called "cultivar" or "fancy" names. According to present regulations these fancy names should be taken from a modern language, for example: *Pelargonium graveolens* 'Lady Plymouth.' Sometimes, however, when a Latin name has long been used for a garden form, it is treated as a fancy name in the same way. Italics are not properly used for such names. To set them off, they are spelled with a capital letter and put in single quotation marks, for example: *Pelargonium quercifolium* 'Pinnatifidum.' If a garden form is known to be a clone (that is, a line maintained through propagation by cuttings only), this may be indicated by using the abbreviation "cl.", an example being *Pelargonium hortorum* cl. 'Mme. Salleron.' Since cuttings comprise the ordinary way of perpetuating cultivars in *Pelargonium*, the abbreviation is not repeated in this book.

Very many of the popular pelargoniums cultivated today are of hybrid origin. To distinguish a hybrid from a wild species, the multiplication sign is used after the generic name. Two common examples are the complex hybrid *P.* × *domesticum* and the more simple hybrid *P.* × *glaucifolium*. The parents of *P.* × *glaucifolium* may be shown by enclosing them in brackets: [*P. gibbosum* × *P. lobatum*]. Because of its awkward appearance when continually repeated in a book of this kind, the multiplication sign is used to indicate hybrids only in the descriptive lists in Part II. At times when the exact parentage or relationship of a hybrid is not known the fancy name may be used alone with the genus, as in *Pelargonium* 'Capri.'

In addition to the names that are used to identify individual kinds of pelargoniums (specific, varietal, and cultivar names) it is sometimes found useful to employ special names to identify particular groups of pelargoniums, such as hybrid groups that may include within themselves the offspring of several species. The botanist and horticulturist do this when they refer to *Pelargonium hortorum* and *Pelargonium domesticum*; nontechnical people do the same when they speak of "garden geraniums" (*P. hortorum*) or "ivy geraniums" (*P. peltatum*). Such group names are a great convenience; it is right that we should use them but we must always remember that they are general rather than specific in their application.

AUTHORITIES FOR NAMES

In Part II, readers will also find abbreviations of botanists' names following the name for species or Latin-named hybrids. These abbreviations (given in full on page 177) constitute the botanical authority, and although they are not actually a part of the name they tell something of its history.

Many of the pelargoniums were first described as species of *Geranium* by Linnaeus or other early botanists and were later placed in *Pelargonium* by others writers. The authority is used to show who first described the species and who first put it in the right genus if this was not done in the beginning. Seeing the name *Pelargonium denticulatum* Jacq., we know that Jacquin first described the species in what is considered today as the correct genus. *Pelargonium cordifolium* (Cav.) Curt. shows that Curtis recognized that the plant originally described as *Geranium cordifolium* by Cavanilles belonged to *Pelargonium* and transferred it to its rightful genus.

Many of the species known to Linnaeus and described by him as *Geranium* were transferred to *Pelargonium* by the French botanist L'Héritier in an unpublished manuscript and in letters available to the compilers of *Hortus Kewensis,* a catalogue of plants grown at The Royal Botanic Gardens at Kew, England, published by William Aiton in 1789. Although Aiton actually proposed these names in his own book, he gave credit to L'Héritier. This is shown by connecting the two names with the Latin "ex" (from) as in *Pelargonium capitatum* (L.) L'Hér. ex Ait.

SYNONYMS AND ERRONEOUS NAMES

Readers may occasionally find that a familiar pelargonium is mentioned under a name that is strange to them. It is now an established principle that the first name given to the species in proper form must be used for it and that there can be no duplication of names in any genus. It is because of this eminently sensible rule (though it is sometimes difficult to apply) that name changes are sometimes necessary. Merely because a pelargonium has been grown and known under one name for a long time does not prove that it is the right one. New names are also sometimes necessitated by the fact that the name given to one pelargonium already belongs (by virtue of earlier publication) to another kind. Misidentifications may also result in the erroneous association of a name with a plant. When plants have been known by more than one name the synonyms and erroneous names are listed with the correct name in Part II of this book.

The rules apply to fancy names as well and the same name should not be used for more than one cultivated form even if it is attached to a different species in the same genus. Where the same horticultural name exists for two or more pelargoniums belonging to different groups within the genus, such as the name "Thibaut" (which in various forms has been applied to cultivars of *Pelargonium domesticum*, *P. hortorum*, *P. peltatum*, and a hybrid of *P. hortorum* × *P. peltatum*), the name in question is retained for the plant to which it was given first. If doubt exists as to which plant is deserving of the name under the priority principle, then a choice is made according to the best available evidence, and the others are given new names. Whenever this situation arises it must be recognized that the choice is arbitrary and evidence may later be uncovered that necessitates a further change.

In the case of 'Madame Thibaut' evidence indicates that this name was used first for a *P. domesticum* cultivar developed by Arthur Malet in France and first mentioned in *L'Horticulteur Français* in 1867. Later, in error, another plant was also given the name of 'Madame Thibaut.' Since this duplicated the former name, the second plant is now more correctly called 'Sweet William,' an alternative name which had been ascribed to it.

There are, in addition, other clones named after members of the Thibaut family, but these are distinguished through the use of a Christian name or other title, such as 'Monsieur Thibaut' for a *P. hortorum* cultivar (named by Lemoine in *L'Horticulteur Français* in 1869) and 'Louise Thibaut' for a form of *P. peltatum* described in the *Wiener Illustrierte Gartenzeitung* in 1882.

An even more complicated situation is one in which a correct name becomes attached to the wrong plant. An example is seen in the case of *Pelargonium grossularioides*, which is often erroneously known as *P. parviflorum*. There is—or was—a true *Pelargonium parviflorum*, but it is now considered to be the same as *P. ferulaceum*, a species not in cultivation and not at all like *P. grossularioides*. The latter has very small flowers and was once illustrated by Andrews as *Geranium parviflorum*. Presumably someone recognized that the plant pictured by Andrews agreed with plants of *P. grossularioides* growing in his garden and simply used his name instead of the earlier and correct one. The confusion is made even worse because the name *P. grossularioides* has somehow become associated erroneously with a form of *Pelargonium crispum* which is thought to have leaves resembling a gooseberry. Since *grossularioides* means gooseberry-like, the error is easily understood.

THE BASIS FOR NAMES

Technical names, both botanical and horticultural, are based on published descriptions and generally on dried specimens of plants which are filed in herbaria in various parts of the world. In order that botanists and horticulturists may apply correct names to the pelargoniums we grow, it is necessary to compare them with such specimens (when available) and with the published descriptions and illustrations.

When naming new pelargoniums it is most important to publish the new name in a recognized botanical or horticultural periodical or book together with an adequate description and, if possible, a good illustration. If possible also, pressed and dried specimens of the newly named plant should be filed in one or more herbaria.

Because of the obvious pitfalls that beset those who search literature and herbaria in their efforts to apply correct names to plants, certainty is not always possible. The author makes no claim of finality for her work. She has searched the repositories of botanical and horticultural knowledge that were available to her and after carefully weighing the evidence has arrived at certain conclusions regarding which names belong to which pelargonium. These are presented and used in this book.

Chapter 6

HISTORY OF GERANIUMS

To trace the cultivated geranium historically from its hazy past through the era when new forms were first being introduced, then down to the present day, it is necessary to give attention to its successive names. During the early part of this period, the subject of botany was slowly evolving as a science, and as it progressed, lasting changes were gradually made in plant nomenclature.

When herbs were widely used in medicine, herbalists noticed the ripened fruit of the wild geranium of England and Europe and its resemblance to the bill of a crane or stork. The English herbalist, John Gerard, wrote the following of one of the common species, *Geranium columbinum*, in 1597: ". . . after which [flowering] is the seede set togither like the head and bill of a birde, whereupon it was called Cranes bill, or Storkes bill, as are also all the others of his kinde."

As the first pelargoniums were introduced from South Africa, a few in Holland and England about 1632 but more particularly from 1690 onward, the name "cranesbill" was still used for the native geranium of Europe, while the name "storksbill" was gradually confined to the South African species that were welcomed for their scented leaves and brighter flowers.

EARLY ATTEMPTS AT NAMING

The Latin form of cranesbill or *Geranium*, derived from the Greek *geranos*, meaning a crane, had descended from Dioscorides of ancient

26

Greece and was used by the herbalists in addition to the vernacular name. The Latinized form of storksbill, or *Pelargonium*, taken from the Greek *pelargos*, or stork, was mentioned by James Petiver before 1718. In 1732, Johann Jacob Dillenius spoke of the difference between the South African and European plants in *Hortus Elthamensis*. Although he, too, mentioned the name *Pelargonium* he did not use it. A few years later, however, the Dutch botanist Johannes Burman distinguished between *Geranium* and *Pelargonium* in his book on rare African plants (1738).

When Linnaeus wrote *Species Plantarum* in 1753, he put the cranesbills and storksbills together in *Geranium*, as did Burman's son, Nicolaus Laurentius Burman, in a little book on geraniums, *Specimen Botanicum de Geraniis*, written in 1759. It was not until 1789, when William Aiton published *Hortus Kewensis* as a catalogue of the plants growing in the Royal Botanic Gardens at Kew, England, that *Pelargonium* was clearly established as a separate genus with the credit given to a French botanist, Charles Louis L'Héritier.

When *Hortus Kewensis* was being written, L'Héritier had already prepared the manuscript to accompany a series of handsome plates illustrating cranesbills, storksbills, and a third kind to be known later as heronsbills. The plates appeared alone in 1792 under the title *Geraniologia*. Although the manuscript itself was never published, its contents were known to botanists in England through letters from L'Héritier. Thus Aiton had access to this important material. L'Héritier proposed that the name *Geranium* be retained for the group of hardy plants largely native in the north temperate zone. For some very similar plants native in Europe he proposed the name *Erodium*, taken from the Greek *erodios*, a heron, from which has come "heronsbill."

The name *Pelargonium* was taken over from the earlier writers and given to the genus which is largely native in South Africa, and which is the subject of this book. The three genera were classified later under the family name Geraniaceae.

Of twenty-nine species of *Pelargonium* illustrated by L'Héritier, the following are in cultivation today: *P. cordatum* (now called *P. cordifolium*), *P. cotyledonis*, *P. crassicaule*, *P. glaucum*, *P. graveolens*, *P. glutinosum*, *P. pinnatum*, *P. quercifolium*, *P. radula* (now called *P. radens*), *P. scabrum*, *P. tetragonum* and *P. vitifolium*.

In addition to those illustrated, a number of others were listed by

Aiton and among these the following are also in cultivation: *P. acetosum*, *P. alchemilloides*, *P. angulosum*, *P. bicolor*, *P. capitatum*, *P. carnosum*, *P. fulgidum*, *P. gibbosum*, *P. inquinans*, *P. odoratissimum*, *P. papilionaceum*, *P. peltatum* and *P. zonale*.

FIRST INTRODUCTIONS

Plants such as L'Héritier was eventually responsible for naming *Pelargonium* were first known in European horticulture a century and a half before his day. As early as 1632 a plant believed to have been *Pelargonium triste* had been obtained from South Africa by John Tradescant and flowered in England. Its mention in Johnson's edition of Gerard's Herbal as *Geranium indicum*, 1633, is apparently the first published record in England. At about the same time, or perhaps before, one or more species are also thought to have been grown in Holland. In the fine garden of Dr. James Sherard at Eltham, England, half a dozen species grew in 1732, and Philip Miller, author of the *Gardeners Dictionary*, listed twenty species of African geraniums (*Pelargonium*) in 1733. At least three of these, *P. alchemilloides*, *P. cucullatum*, and *P. capitatum* (the rose-scented storksbill of ancestral English gardens) were cultivated before 1700 in herb and "physick" gardens. By 1800 numerous species were being cultivated in England and many new forms had appeared.

The number of species recognized today varies according to the author. A reasonable estimate appears to be about three hundred. This figure is based on the number of species and natural varieties described by Knuth in Engler's *Das Pflanzenreich*, 1912, and the new species listed in *Index Kewensis* since that time.

FIRST RECORDED HYBRIDS

When Henry C. Andrews published his *Monograph of the Genus Geranium* in two volumes in 1805, organized botany was still in its infancy and hybrids were created and introduced without thought of their parental origins. It is, therefore, understandable that Andrews described hybrids as varieties. However, intensive hybridizing is noted and the illustrations are worthy of study, as many plants show the transmission of characters from parents to progeny.

The method of selecting parents with the hope of transmitting to the progeny the best qualities of each, and recording the crosses, began about 1815. Sir Richard Hoare was a leader in establishing the new scientific method of breeding.

The earliest hybrid appears to be a cross between *P. inquinans* and *P. zonale* that was illustrated by Dillenius in 1731 and later named *Geranium hybridum* by Linnaeus. The oldest known scented hybrids in cultivation are *P. fragrans* and *P. nervosum*. *P. fragrans* arose, apparently as a chance hybrid, in the Botanical Garden in Berlin. *P. nervosum* was first noticed in England, but its parentage could not be determined. Andrews in 1805 illustrated a series of variants derived from *P. crispum* as *Geranium citriodorum*. Some of these probably represent the plants properly called *P. citrosum* today but better known in gardens as *P. citriodorum*. If Knuth's assumption that *P. apiifolium* is a hybrid is correct, then it is the oldest thick-stemmed deciduous clone * that has descended to us.

Because of its large and brilliant flowers, *P. fulgidum* was more frequently used in hybridizing than any other pelargonium at first. Jenkinson and Colville of England raised hybrids of *P. capitatum* crossed with *P. ignescens* (a derivative of *P. fulgidum*) in 1818 to obtain *P. concolor*. To this day we grow plants that appear to be of similar parentage, such as *Pelargonium* 'Concolor Lace' and the lavender-flowered 'Lavender Lace,' which is apparently a reversion to the flower color of its *P. capitatum* parent.

Tuberous-rooted and other distinctive species were also hybridized at an early date. Among those not previously mentioned are the black-flowered *P. glaucifolium* and *P. rutaceum* and the red-flowered *P. ardens*.

The first published records of pelargonium hybrids are contained in *Geraniaceae* by Robert Sweet. This work was published in five volumes, issued between 1820 and 1830. The five hundred illustrations include species, hybrids of known parentage, and many hybrids of chance origin. Among those illustrated, the following hybrids have descended to us: *P. blandfordianum*, *P. nervosum*, *P. scarboroviae* and *P. stapletonii*. Species include *P. alternans*, *P. abrotanifolium*, *P. carnosum*, *P. denticulatum*, *P. pinnatum*, *P. praemorsum*, *P. papil-*

---

* A clone, as explained on page 22, is a plant perpetuated from generation to generation by vegetative propagation; in the case of geraniums, by cuttings.

ionaceum and *P. reniforme*. Sweet's illustration numbers are cited with the descriptions of *Pelargonium* in Part II of this book for the benefit of those who have access to his volumes and who may wish to study illustrations of pelargoniums rarely depicted elsewhere.

Along with the progress of botany as a science, amateur activity with plants also increased in the early nineteenth century. Gardening interests were stimulated by the founding of the Horticultural Society of London (later to become The Royal Horticultural Society) in 1804, and by the increasing numbers of horticultural magazines which were published in many countries of Europe. By these means ornamental plants were brought to the attention of the people. As a secondary result, plant growing became a profitable industry, and nurseries arose throughout most countries of Europe.

Even though descriptions of hybrids had been published earlier, plant breeding was not understood until about 1815, and then by only a select few. Not until 1840 did amateurs begin to comprehend selective hybridizing. Since this period the preservation of species through cultivation and the development of better hybrids has become centered more and more in the amateur.

PELARGONIUMS IN AMERICA

The date when pelargoniums were first introduced into America cannot be definitely established. Surely, our early colonists were too much concerned with food plants to give time and attention to tender ornamental plants. Published records inform us that "geranium" *seeds* were sent to John Bartram in Philadelphia, 1760, and that potted geraniums were sold in the same city in 1789.

Thomas Jefferson sent plants called *P. gibbosum* and *P. maculatum* from France to John Bartram in 1786. The term "maculatum" as then used in France refers to what we know today technically as *P. domesticum*. In 1791 Jefferson was growing geraniums in the window recesses of his White House apartment.

A painting by Rembrandt Peale in 1801 portrays Rubens Peale holding the "first geranium *plant*" brought to America. This plant is a *P. hortorum* variety with single, scarlet flowers. "A red flowered geranium in a green-painted tub" is recorded as having been brought to Canada in 1825.

By 1830 hundreds of geraniums (*P. hortorum*) were being grown in the Eastern States; and by 1840 pelargoniums (*P. domesticum*) were being raised in quantity for the "parlor window." After 1840 pelargoniums of all classes marched westward with the pioneers.

Importations of modern *P. hortorum, P. domesticum* and *P. peltatum* varieties (more properly known as cultivars) were chiefly relied upon for increase of stock in this country until our Government's quarantine regulations restricted the general importation of plants. Many of these earlier imported plants are standard varieties even today. Their mutations have added to the sum total and they have also provided our hybridists with choice material for further developments.

Among the leading American hybrids and those who developed or raised them are the following: By the late Richard Diener—'Giant Venus' and 'Richard Diener' (*domesticum*); 'Elenore Rober' and 'Mrs. William Kent' (*hortorum*); and 'Dieners Lavender' (*peltatum*). By the late Mrs. Clara Sue Jarrett—'Sue Jarrett,' 'Baby,' 'Ruth Ellen Kellogg,' and 'Jarretts Moonbeam' (all *domesticum* hybrids). By the late Ernest Rober—'Marie Rober' and 'Gypsy Queen' (*domesticum*); 'Edee' and 'Maria Wilkes' (*hortorum*); 'Cayucas,' 'Cliff House' and 'Modesto' (*peltatum*), and numerous *P. hortorum* dwarfs.

Later developments include: By Stafford L. Jory—'Berkeley Brilliant,' 'Berkeley Belle,' and 'Berkeley Raspberry' (*hortorum*). By Howard Kerrigan—'Don Juan,' 'Rhapsody,' and 'Spring Song' (*domesticum*). By William H. Bohannon—'Queen of Hearts' and 'Royal Velvet' (*domesticum*). By A. H. Cassidy—'Grace Armstrong,' 'Peach Blow,' 'Red Moon,' and 'Vida Burke' (*domesticum*). By L. H. and W. S. Brown—'Chalee,' 'Jungle Night,' and 'Orange Tanager' (*domesticum*). William E. Schmidt contributed 'Debutante' and 'Little Rascal' (*domesticum*); 'Lucky Strike' (*peltatum*), and the new distinctive *peltatum* hybrid 'Carnival.' Holmes C. Miller introduced the *hortorum* kinds, 'Flare,' 'Delight,' and 'Puff.' Scented-leaved introductions include 'Village Hill Oak' and 'Codys Fragrans' by Dorcas Brigham; and 'Logee,' 'Fringed Oak,' and 'Joy Lucille' by the late Ernest Logee.

In the past few years Milton H. Arndt, a pelargonium fancier who has made a hobby of hybridizing, has developed not only new individual plants but groups of distinctive plants. Among his outstanding achievements are the following:

1—Large-growing geraniums (*P. hortorum*) with colored velvetlike leaves, represented by 'Rusty Fire' and 'Russet.'

2—A group of smaller-growing *P. hortorum* cultivars with colored leaves of unusual patterns. The various color combinations in each leaf, and the miniature size of the plants distinguish them from all others.

3—About 500 dwarf *P. hortorum* cultivars, grouped according to size: (a) maximum height to 4 inches; (b) maximum height to 6 inches; (c) maximum height 8 to 10 inches. The foliage varies in the different plants in texture, lobing, diversity of green from light to dark, zoning and color of flowers so that each plant is a distinctive one. A new race of miniatures which he has developed are unlike any pelargoniums previously seen, for they include distinctive coloring in their leaves.

4—Distinctive *P. hortorum* cultivars such as 'Patricia Audette,' 'Olivia Kuser,' 'Wicked Lady,' 'Peaches and Cream,' and 'Tobey.'

5—Scented-leaved developments, including *P. crispum* 'French Lace,' and derivatives of *P. fragrans* with various pleasing aromatic scents.

In addition to his hybridizing efforts, Mr. Arndt has introduced the first known double-flowered *P. domesticum* variety, and a pelargonium developed in Japan with daisylike flowers. He has also been doing some interesting work with colchicine. Among the offspring from some colchicine-treated *hortorum* clones, for instance, he has obtained forms resembling not only the recognized parents, *P. zonale* and *P. inquinans*, but many resembling other species as well. This, he believes, is good evidence that *Pelargonium hortorum* has much more than these two species in its background.

PART II

Descriptions

Chapter I

PELARGONIUM HORTORUM

Our modern garden geraniums have evolved over a period of more than two centuries. Today they are widely varying plants giving evidence of their mixed heredity.

THE GARDEN GERANIUM IN HISTORY

The mixture of species in *Pelargonium hortorum* goes back to about 1732 when a plant that Dillenius called a variety of *Pelargonium inquinans* (or in his own phrase, *Geranium Africanum arborescens, Malvae folio pingui, flore coccineo varietas*) grew in Dr. James Sherard's garden at Eltham, England. This variety, which now bears the name *Pelargonium hybridum*, is supposed by some authorities to represent the first cross between *P. inquinans* and *P. zonale*, the primal parents of the garden geranium.

Since plants of the two original species, with their small red flowers, were first brought from Cape Colony, where their descendants may still be seen in the wild, they have been carried far in appearance as well as in distance. From dwarfs a few inches high they now run to man-size specimens, and the colors cover a wide range with subtle gradations. Other species, and certainly *P. peltatum*, have doubtless entered into the parentage of this group, to which L. H. Bailey gave the name *Pelargonium hortorum* in 1900. During the course of evolution these plants were also known at various times as Horseshoe and Fish geraniums, Hybrid Perpetuals, Zonates and Zonals.

The primal parents and early hybrids had single flowers of scarlet, crimson or red. Although this group is older than *P. domesticum*, its development was not as rapid at first. Early writers have suggested that its culture was not so well understood; a contributory reason for early lack of enthusiasm may have been the unvarying color of the flowers. More than a hundred years elapsed after the introduction of the species before flower colors other than red shades became available. After 1830 the color range increased slightly.

Of major importance was the development of "Nosegay" geraniums begun in England in the 1850's. The colorful flowers captured the imagination of professional and amateur gardeners. By 1870 Nosegays reached a state of perfection not hitherto known. The flower clusters became more globular in form; the rounded petals gave the flowers a larger appearance; the color range increased; and the flowering period became lengthened.

About 1870 Paul Bruant initiated the production of a new strain which in France was called "Gros Bois." In America it became known as the "Bruant race." These forms are listed commercially today as "French types" and differ from the standard cultivars in that the stems are thicker, the leaves coarser, and the flower-stalks thicker and often shorter. These characters give the plants a more vigorous appearance as opposed to the slender stems and generally more refined appearance of the usual forms. Representatives of French types of the hortorum group in cultivation include 'Mrs. E. G. Hill,' dating from the 1880's; 'Alphonse Ricard,' the 1890's; the distinctive 'Monsieur Emile David,' 1875; and 'Suzanne,' with distinctive broadly dark-zoned leaves, introduced about 1900.

Although French types are readily distinguished from the others, there are intermediate forms which cannot be classified so easily. I have in mind the darkest-flowered geranium, 'Nuit Poitevine,' which is a standard type, and 'Will Rogers,' which is classified as a French type; the flowers and leaves in each plant are very similar but the stems in the French type appear to be slightly thicker. It is quite possible that the original plant mutates slightly in two directions.

Semidouble flowers were known in 1817. However, double flowers as we know them today were introduced by Victor Lemoine in 1864 after many years of hybridizing.

In England during the 1860's mutants (sports) arose with single flowers of combined colors; these plants were called "Apple Blossom" geraniums. As other color combinations arose, each plant in turn was called a "New Apple Blossom." This name was a general one for any plant of this group in which the petal margins were brighter than the centers.

Colorful flowers with small white centers were known in England a few decades before flowers with conspicuous white centers arose in France. Currently grown "Phlox Eye" geraniums appear to be reversions to English "White-eyed" geraniums among the early Nosegay geraniums of the 1850's.

In 1886, a Monsieur Herlaut of Mirande, France, raised from seed a plant which differed from any other known geranium. Christened 'Souvenir de Mirande,' this seedling produced single flowers in which the lower petals were bright carmine-rose shading to white in the center, and the upper petals were white edged with carmine.

Other flowers of blended colors, streaks or stripes were developed by Bruant about 1890, and are said to have been derived from colorful flowers with white centers. By blended colors we mean the mingling of two or three unrelated hues to a point where they cannot be defined clearly; this character is best described in terms of overtones and undertones.

Carnation-flowered geraniums in the *P. hortorum* group were first known in England in 1847. Toothed petals also occur in derivatives of *P. peltatum.*

"Bird's-egg" geraniums originated in France about 1890. These are characterized by a profusion of pin-point dots on the petals.

Cactus-flowered geraniums are recognized by their quilled petals and are represented by the type called 'Poinsettia,' which is a mutant of obscure origin.

Variegated green-and-white-leaved geraniums were known and illustrated in England in 1734. The oldest clone of this kind which is now in cultivation is 'Mountain of Snow,' which originated in England in 1855.

The earliest traceable bronze-leaved geranium is 'The Moor,' which was first seen in England about 1860. The leaves are described as having "sulphur disk and margin, zone rich reddish chocolate."

Yellow- or golden-margined leaves were known in England before 1830. These arise spontaneously from time to time.

Colored-leaved or "Tricolor" geraniums were the special concern of Peter Grieve and the English firm of Henderson during the 1850's. Among Grieve's developments, 'Mrs. Pollock,' 'Lady Cullum,' and 'Miss Burdett Coutts' are still in cultivation.

Dwarfs occur spontaneously in all groups and were known in England before 1800. Hybridizing efforts have been directed largely toward developing dwarf forms of *P. hortorum* varieties; in a lesser degree *P. domesticum*. Dwarf cultivars of *Pelargonium hortorum* from Europe include 'Black Vesuvius,' England; 'Mme. Fournier,' France; and 'Kleiner Liebling' ('Little Darling' in translation), Germany. The English and French dwarfs have been used extensively in the development of American dwarf varieties.

PELARGONIUM HORTORUM OF THE PRESENT

P. × hortorum L. H. Bailey—Plants of this group vary from dwarf to very tall but are characterized by their softly woody, somewhat succulent or fleshy stems, scalloped, nearly circular leaves, long-spurred flowers in a compact, rounded umbel, and petals nearly equal in size and shape. The leaves are often zoned or variegated in various shades as mentioned in the history of the group.

The earliest hybrids, with their red, scarlet or crimson flowers, have been developed by horticulturists into plants with colors ranging into the following diverse groups:

1—Many shades of the original reds, varying in degree of density and intensity.

2—From red through vivid rose-pink, pink, blush-pink, to faintly tinted white and pure white.

3—From scarlet with its barely perceptible inclusion of yellow, through vermilion, brassy orange, to orange. On the lighter-colored side we have apricot, salmon, salmon-pink, peach, and ivory.

4—From crimson with a faint suggestion of blue ingredient, through carmine, cerise, American Beauty red, magenta, ruby-red, to several shades approximating purple. The lighter colors graduate through old-rose, violet-rose, orchid-pink, lavender and lavender-tinted white.

5—Blended colors in addition to self-colors, and combinations of two or three different colors in the same flower.

Mere designation of colors cannot convey the subtle gradations of which the eye is pleasantly aware. Therefore, in the paragraphs which follow, an attempt has been made to describe, rather than name, the flower colors so that the reader may visualize the appearance of each variety. White-flowered geraniums appear on page 39 followed by "phlox-eye," page 41; pink and rose-pink, page 41; violet, lavender and orchid-pink, page 42; shrimp, salmon, peach, and apricot in light shades, page 43; and in deeper shades, page 45; orange and apricot-orange, page 47; red with white markings, page 48; red, scarlet and vermilion, page 49; crimson to purple, page 52.

Some of the more unusual flower types are grouped together: carnation-like, page 54; rosebud, page 55; cactus-flowered, page 55; bird's-egg, page 56. Dwarfs and miniatures are listed separately on pages 61 and 62. Variegated or colored leaves come in several combinations: variegated green and white, page 56; yellow or golden-yellow, page 57; smooth bronze-green, page 60; velvetlike bronze-green, page 60; brightly colored or tricolor, page 58; dwarfs with colored leaves, page 65 and some new large forms with colored leaves, page 66.

SELECTED CULTIVARS OF PELARGONIUM HORTORUM

(Geraniums of Gardeners)

Those designated as the "French type" have extra large clusters of large, rounded flowers; the leaves, about 5 inches in diameter, are of heavy texture with strongly marked nerves; the stems are thick and fleshy.

White-Flowered Geraniums

'Alaska'—French type, flowers single to semidouble, white faintly lavender tinged. California.

'Ambrosia'—Large clusters of single white flowers; buds long, pointed; petals curled. Arndt, 1948.

'Gregersons White'—Flowers large, double, white; not as loosely clustered as those of 'Ryecroft White.' California.

'Marguerite de Layre'—Flowers medium large, single, white, faintly pink-tinged at base of petals. France, 1889.

'Mme. Buchner'—(syns. 'White Madonna,' 'Alba Plena')—Habit of growth compact; flowers medium large, double, white, faintly green-tinged at base of petals. France, 1876.

'Olivia Kuser'—Large, habit of growth vigorous; flowers very large, single, pure white; petals rounded and overlapping. Arndt, 1950. A distinctive new variety with long flower stalks.

'Ryecroft White'—French type; habit compact; flowers large, semi-double, white. Ryecroft Nursery, England, 1890's.

'Snowball'—Flowers medium large, double, white, in compact clusters. Originated in Ohio.

'White Glory'—('Gregersons White' × 'Olivia Kuser')—French type; flower clusters large, long-stalked; flowers large, semidouble, pure white. Developed by Arndt, 1950.

'White Magic'—Small to medium large; flowers large, semidouble, white. Miller, 1950.

White Flowers Tinged or Marked with Color

'Allure'—Large clusters of single white flowers with heavy pink veining; flower buds long, pink. Arndt, 1948.

'Always'—Flowers large, double, creamy white flushed with shrimp pink. Miller, 1948.

'Carmel'—Flowers single, white with narrow margins of rose pink. Schmidt, about 1947.

'Cinderella'—Flower clusters small; flowers single, pink, white at the margins. Originated in England, 1880's. A popular variety in New England.

'Inspiration'—French type; habit small; flower clusters medium in size; flowers large, semidouble, creamy white flushed with pale salmon. Miller, 1949.

'Jean Oberle'—(syn. 'Buxton')—Vigorous; flowers double, pale peach pink shading to white at margins of petals. France, 1906.

'Lady Brooks'—French type, flowers large, single, shading from white to pale pink, paler at margins.

'La Fraîcheur' (syn. 'Canadian Pink and White')—Plant medium large; flowers medium large, double, white with rose pink at margins of petals. France, 1868.

'Georgia Belle'—A distinctive single, white flowered variety with deep peach and brown veining. Arndt, 1947.

'Patricia Audette'—Large and vigorous; flower clusters on long stems; flowers very large, single, soft pale pink, white from the center to base of lower petals. Distinctive. Arndt, 1948.

'**Pink Shimmer**'—Leaves dark green, ruffled; flowers large, single, white with a pencil line of pink on very edge of petals. Arndt, 1947.

'**Pink Snow**'—Flowers single to semidouble, white with blush pink margins. A mutant raised by Dorcas Brigham.

'**Tobey**'—Habit large, vigorous; flowers double, very large, pale creamy pink and white; the petals are distinctively long, waved and curled. A mutant of 'Peaches and Cream' raised by Arndt, 1950.

Phlox-Eye Geraniums

"Phlox-eye" geraniums are characterized by small, single flowers in which a uniformly round eye in the center differs in color from the surrounding area. Among the numerous kinds in cultivation are the following:

'**Edee**'—Tall; flowers orchid pink with white eye. Ernest Rober, California, 1930's.

'**Rose Phlox**'—Flowers soft rose pink with darker eye. Rober, 1940's.

'**Pale Phlox**'—Flowers white with rose pink eye. California.

'**Pink Phlox**'—Flowers pale pink with deeper pink eye. California.

'**Phlox Eye**'—Flowers white with vermilion eye. California.

Pink and Rose Pink Flowers

'**Alice de la Verne**'—Flowers single, deep rose pink, white at center. Rober, 1930's.

'**Ann Sothern**'—Flowers medium large, single, violet rose shading to white in center. California.

'**Berkeley Blush**'—Flowers single, pink, blush pink at margins of petals. Stafford L. Jory, California.

'**Frances Perkins**'—Flower clusters large; flowers semidouble, clear rose pink. Perkins, 1920's. 'California Beauty' is similar, differing only in the lighter shade of the flowers.

'**Gertrude Pearson**'—Habit compact; leaves velvetlike; flowers large, single, clear rose-pink with white throat. England, 1890's.

'**Madame Barney**' (syns. 'Kunze,' 'Pink Barney')—Plant small; flowers small, double, rose pink. France, 1890's.

'**Monsieur Thibaut**' (erroneously called 'Madame Thibaut')—Flowers double, pink with faint salmon tint, white at center and margins of petals. Developed by Victor Lemoine and named for Mr., not for Mrs., Thibaut. France, 1869.

'Mrs. Richard F. Gloede' (syns. 'Los Angeles,' 'Thomas Meehan')—French type; flowers large, double, old rose with slight salmon tint. Distinctive. Veitch & Son, England, about 1902.

'Mrs. Brown Potter'—Plant small; flowers single to semidouble, clear rose pink. England, about 1900.

'Multicolor'—Flowers single, medium large in good-sized clusters, pale pink changing through rose pink to old rose. California.

'Old Rose'—Habit medium; flowers large, semidouble, old rose. Miller, 1948.

'Pink Phenomenal' (syn. 'Pink Giant')—French type; medium large; flower clusters long-stalked; flowers large, semidouble, rose pink with white in center. England, 1936.

'Pink Satin'—Flower clusters large on long stalks; flowers large, single, light pink. Arndt, 1948.

'Porcelain Rose'—Habit medium; leaves lightly zoned; flowers large, double, in medium-large clusters; named for the soft rose color shown in the British Horticultural Colour Chart; petals curled. Distinctive. Developed by Frank Moreau in Freehold, N. J., 1949.

'Romany'—Medium-large habit of growth; leaves zoned; flowers large, double, salmon red blended with old rose. Miller, 1950.

'Shirley Summers'—Flowers medium large, double, rose pink with white center and irregular white margins; occasional flowers all white or all rose pink. California.

'Summer Charm'—Flowers large, single in large clusters; flowers carmine pink, deeper toward margins, white at center. Introduced by Paul J. Howard in California.

Violet, Lavender, and Orchid-Pink Flowers

'Berthe de Presilly'—Flowers double, silvery orchid pink shading to almost white in center. Bruant, France, 1889.

'Helen Van Pelt Wilson'—Flowers medium large, single light orchid pink. Rober, 1945.

'Jean Viaud'—French type; flowers large, semidouble, rose pink shading through orchid pink to white center. France, 1891.

'Lavender Lady'—French type; clusters large; flowers double, rose pink with lavender tint, white at center. California.

'Maria Wilkes' (syn. 'Springfield Shell Pink')—Flowers large, double, shell pink with orchid tints toward the white center. Rober, about 1945.

'Lavender Ricard' (a mutant of 'Alphonse Ricard')—French type; flowers large, semidouble, rose pink with lavender overtones, white center. California.

'Lavender Supreme'—French type; flowers medium large, semidouble, lavender pink. California.

'Memories'—Flowers large, semidouble, pale orchid pink. Miller, 1950.

'Persian Rose'—Habit medium large; leaves broadly zoned; flowers single, old rose with violet overtones, tiny darker dots in the petals. California.

'Single Lavender'—Flowers large, single, orchid pink shading to deeper tones toward the white center, occasional bird's-egg dots in lower petals. Rober, about 1944.

Light Shrimp, Salmon, Peach, and Apricot Flowers

'Advance'—Flowers medium large, single, pale salmon with buff overtones.

'Alice Lemon'—Plant small; leaves zoned; flowers single, pale salmon deepening toward margins. 1920, California.

'Beauté Poitevine'—French type; leaves dark zoned; flowers large, semidouble, salmon pink, paler toward center. An outstanding variety of its class. Developed by Bruant in France, 1869.

'Beauty of Jersey' (syn. 'Countess of Jersey')—Habit medium, compact; flowers large, single, pale shrimp pink. England, 1893.

'Coral Gem'—Large flower clusters held on long stalks; flower buds long and pointed; flowers coral pink blending into the white center. Arndt, 1947.

'Doris Kenyon'—Flowers large, single, delicate salmon, paler at the margins. Rober 1930's.

'Double La France'—Medium tall, bushy; clusters large, compact; flowers large, double, blended soft rose pink and salmon. This is a double-flowered form of 'La France' developed by Jean Sisley in Lyons, France, 1870's.

'Elenore Rober'—Tall, French type; flowers medium large, single, salmon, paler at the margins. Diener, about 1935.

'Enchantress Cameo'—French type; flowers large, double, shrimp pink, slightly paler at the margins. A 'Fiat' mutant. California.

'Enchantress Supreme'—French type; flowers double, salmon pink. A mutant of a 'Fiat' mutant raised by Wilson Brothers in Indiana, 1945.

'Fiat Enchantress'—French type; compact habit; flowers large, double, pearly pink, salmon toward the center. 1930.

'Fiat Supreme'—French type; compact habit; flowers large, double, soft shrimp pink. Originated about 1920.

'French Bouquet'—Habit vigorous; flower clusters large; flowers medium large, single, pale shrimp and mauve pink combination. Distinctive in color.

'Gloire de France'—Habit tall; flowers medium large, double, shrimp pink. A French introduction rated as "ordinary" by A. S. Hill in 1889.

'Honeymoon'—Medium size; flowers large, single, apricot salmon, pale shrimp at margins of petals. Variable. California.

'Igor Stravinski'—French type; leaves heavily zoned; flowers large, single, pale shrimp shading to salmon at the center. Rober, 1930's.

'Judy Reed'—Habit compact; flowers medium large, single, ivory pink shading to soft shrimp pink. Arndt, 1948.

'Mme. Jaulin' (syn. 'Apple Blossom')—French type; habit small, bushy; flowers large, cupped, semidouble, delicate pink with a suggestion of pale peach inclusion, almost white at margins of petals. France, 1890's.

'Mrs. Lawrence'—Small, compact; flowers medium large, double, satiny, pale shrimp pink. England, 1906.

'Mrs. Nelson Eddy'—Flower clusters large; flowers medium large, single, ivory pink shading to shrimp pink. California.

'Peaches and Cream'—Vigorous, medium tall; leaves zoned, margins ruffled; flower clusters large; flowers large, double, resembling small camellias in form, soft peach pink with irregular creamy pink margins. Handsome. Arndt, 1948.

'Sunset'—Medium size; flowers large, single, light salmon, slightly deeper salmon in the center, petals suggesting the crinkled appearance of crepe paper. California, 1940's.

'Teddy Roosevelt'—A larger, double and darker-flowered form of 'Mrs. Lawrence.' When first introduced this plant was known as 'Improved Mrs. Lawrence.' California.

'William Humphrey'—Tall and vigorous; leaves deeply zoned and ruffled; umbels large and flat; flowers medium large, single, petals rounded and overlapping, color same as in 'Peaches and Cream.' Arndt, 1948.

Deeper Shades of Salmon, Coral, and Apricot Flowers

'Afterglow'—Flower clusters large; flowers medium large, single, salmon with soft rose overtones. Miller, 1945.

'Angelica'—Medium size; flower buds long and pointed; flowers large, single, vivid apricot pink. Arndt, 1949.

'Annie Vincent'—Medium size, compact; leaves velvety green; flowers semidouble, carmine pink with salmon overtones. Bruant, 1908.

'Barbara Hope'—Habit vigorous, tall; flowers medium large, single, bright salmon pink. Pearson & Son, England, 1899.

'Billie Burke'—French type; flowers large, single, soft pink with salmon tones. Rober, 1930's.

'Cheerio'—Medium size; flowers medium large, single, shading from salmon apricot to salmon coral, white at the center.

'Dolores Costello'—Flower clusters large; flowers large, single salmon and rose pink blended. Lighter in color than 'Afterglow' and slightly more salmon. Rober, about 1935.

'Cocamella'—Flowers very large, single, salmon. Introduced by Dorcas Brigham.

'Coral Barney'—A mutant of 'Madame Barney.' Small; flowers coral pink.

'Dreams'—Flowers large, double, waxlike, soft salmon coral. Miller, 1945.

'Emile Zola' (syns. 'Salmon Queen,' 'Mrs. Hawley')—Flower clusters large; flowers large, single, salmon apricot; petals well rounded. Mutates freely. France, 1890's.

'Fiat'—French type; habit compact; flowers large, double, salmon coral. Numerous excellent mutants of this variety are in cultivation. Schulze, California, 1919.

'Flare'—Flowers large, single, vivid salmon coral to salmon scarlet. Miller, 1945.

'Florence Dempsey' (syn. 'Salmon Queen')—Habit vigorous; flowers large, single, bright salmon with white veins radiating from a white center. Rober, 1935.

'Fred Bean'—Flowers very large, single, waxy, light salmon coral. Howard, 1913.

'Halloween'—Small habit of growth; flower clusters large; flowers large, double, apricot orange, white in center. Miller, 1950.

'Ian MacLaren' (syn. 'Conejo')—Flowers large, single, rose-pink salmon, lighter at the margins. Cannell & Son, England, 1898.

'Irvington Beauty' (syn. 'Rose Pink Fiat')—French type; similar to 'Fiat' in habit of growth; flowers large, semidouble, blended rose pink and salmon. Originated in the 1920's.

'Lady of Spain'—Tall; flowers large, single, soft coral with white center. California, 1947.

'Madame Landry' (syn. 'Salmon Ideal')—French type; flowers large, semidouble, bright apricot salmon, small amount of white at base of petals. France, about 1890.

'Marie Antoinette'—Medium size; flowers large, single, soft salmon apricot. Distinctive. Rober, 1930's.

'Mary Stetson'—Flowers large, single, apricot pink. Rober, 1930.

'May Day'—Flowers large, single, salmon pink with large white center, the color pattern suggesting a pansy. Arndt, 1948.

'Monterey'—Flowers large, double, salmon coral shading through deeper coral to a white center. California.

'Mrs. E. G. Hill'—French type; habit large; leaves zoned; flower clusters large; flowers bright salmon pink paling slightly toward center. The salmon red pedicels (flower stalks) add to the beauty of the luminous flowers. Developed by Bruant in France and introduced in America by "E. G." in the 1880's.

'Pink Abundance'—Leaves light green; flower clusters large; flowers fairly large, double, long stemmed, coral pink. England.

'Marjorie Sprague'—Habit of growth taller and less branched than 'Mme. Landry'; the semidouble flowers more pink and less salmon. Originated in France, 1900's.

'Salmon Ideal'—Flowers large, double, salmon apricot.

'Salmon Supreme'—French type; flowers large, semidouble, light salmon apricot.

'Suzanne Leepre' (syn. 'Aurora Salmon')—French type; compact; flowers medium large, single, deep salmon apricot. Originated in France; introduced into America, 1906.

'Picardy'—Flowers semidouble, distinctive shade of salmon pink.

Orange and Apricot-Orange Flowers

'Autumn'—Clusters large; flowers large, double, apricot orange with white center. Miller, 1948.

'Autumn Glow'—Vigorous; clusters large; flowers large, single, tangerine orange with white eye. Howard.

'Cuba'—Flowers large, single, soft apricot orange. California.

'Golden Gate' (syn. 'El Rey')—Tall; flowers large, single, brassy orange. England, 1890's.

'Glory'—Medium size; flowers large, double, almost orange with a little white at the center. Miller, 1949.

'Indian Summer'—Medium size; clusters large; flowers large, double, mellow apricot orange. Miller, 1948.

'Lave' (syns. 'Springfield Orange,' 'Prince of Orange')—Medium size; flowers double, soft apricot orange, lighter on reverse side of petals. Cannell & Son, England, introduced into America, 1910.

'Maxime Kovalevski' (syns. 'Santa Barbara,' 'Diablo')—Medium size; flower clusters large; flowers large, single, clear bright orange. Developed by Cannell & Son, England, about 1910. Many seedlings of this fine cultivar are being grown, but none equal it in color.

'Nouvelle Aurore' (syn. 'Giant Salmon')—Flower clusters large, flowers large, single, apricot orange with small amount of white in the center. The handsomest of its class. Originated in France, introduced in America, 1915.

'Orange Ricard'—French type; flowers large, semidouble, between orange and scarlet. A mutant of 'Alphonse Ricard.'

'Tango'—Habit vigorous; flowers single, orange. California. Probably a seedling of 'Maxime Kovalevski,' but not as bright and clear in color.

'Sunrise'—Medium size; flower clusters large; flowers large, single, glowing orange with a large white semicircle at the base of the upper petals, a small semicircle at the base of the lower ones. Arndt, 1948.

Red Flowers With White Marking

The amount of white varies considerably in the following group— from small to large white centers, marbled red and white, and white veins and streaks. The prototype of flowers with large white centers as well as the ancestor of blended flowers is 'Souvenir de Mirande.' The original plant was raised from seed by Herlaut of Mirande, France in 1886. Cut flowers of similar plants were exhibited in Buffalo, New York, in 1889; and in the same year the following description appeared in the *American Florist*: "Flowers single, lower petals rosy carmine shading to white at the base, while the upper petals are white merely tipped (edged) with carmine. Distinct from any other previous introduction."

'Alice of Vincennes'—Medium size; flowers large, single, white in the center shading through violet crimson to intense scarlet at the margins. Hill, Indiana, 1901.

'Ambassadeur'—Small; leaves green, ruffled; flowers medium large, single, bright vermilion, white in the center and extending into the upper petals. Arndt, 1948.

'America'—Medium tall; flowers single, scarlet, white at the center and scarlet veined. Introduced in 1899.

'Anastasie Lacadre'—Flower clusters medium large; flowers single, velvety red, small white center. Introduced from France in 1896.

'Berkeley Belle'—Flowers large, petals broadly rounded, light red shading to white center. Developed by Stafford L. Jory.

'Betty Krauss'—French type; leaves large, unzoned; flower clusters large; flowers large, single, upper petals white shading through rose pink to light scarlet at the margins, lower petals light orange scarlet with a small amount of white at the base. Arndt, 1950.

'Carlton Cheerio'—Flowers medium large, single, cherry red with white center. Arndt, 1949.

'Colorado Aggies'—French type of large habit; flowers large, semi-double, orange scarlet to scarlet; suggestive of 'Alphonse Ricard' but the flower color differs slightly. Colorado.

'Dr. Sam Sturgis'—Medium large; flower clusters large and long-stalked; flowers red through marbled red and white to the white throat, reverse side of petals lighter in color. Arndt, 1949.

'Dryden' (syns. 'Lady Dryden,' 'Santa Monica')—Small; flowers single, scarlet shading to white center. Originated in England; introduced into America, 1899.

'Double Dryden'—Small; flowers double, coral white at base of petals, shading to vermilion and paling at the margins. Introduced in America, 1902.

'Harriet Ann'—Flowers large, single, red shading to large white center.

'Jules Vasseur'—Habit tall and slender; flowers large, double, red, white at the throat and sometimes streaking into the red. Introduced from France in 1906.

Red, Scarlet, and Vermilion Flowers

'Alexian Beauty'—Suggestive of 'S. A. Nutt' (described below) but of better and neater growing habit; flower clusters larger and longer stalked; flowers medium large, double, rich velvety red.

'Alphonse Ricard'—French type; flowers large, semidouble, scarlet. A popular French cultivar introduced in 1896.

'Berkeley Brilliant'—Flowers large, single, vivid deep scarlet. Jory, California.

'Carlton Fire'—A standard cultivar of medium large growth, bushy, leaves light green, faintly zoned; flowers medium large, double, bright crimson, center petals curled. A good commercial form. Arndt, 1952.

'Crabbe'—Flowers large, single, vermilion, becoming lighter toward the small white throat. Introduced from England, 1900. A double-flowered form was introduced from England in 1907.

'Dorothea Louise'—Small; flowers single, intense red with small white eye in the center. Miller, 1945.

'Fireglow'—French type; medium large; leaves zoned; flowers large, double, vivid scarlet. Miller, 1947.

'Gallant'—French type; growing habit somewhat smaller than 'Alphonse Ricard'; flowers medium large, semidouble, scarlet. Miller.

'Hall Caine'—Habit compact; flowers very large, single, cherry red. Developed by Cannell & Son, England. Introduced in America, 1901.

'Helen Michell'— ('Alphonse Ricard' × 'Jean Viaud')—French type, large; flowers large, semidouble, luminous scarlet. Developed by Henry J. Michell Co. 1913.

'Herrick'—Habit small; flowers large, single, velvety orange scarlet. Introduced from England in 1898.

'Highlight'—Vigorous; flowers medium large, single, white at the center shading through rose to rose red at the edge; margins of petals lightly orange flushed. Schmidt, 1946.

'Isabel'—French type; flower clusters large; flowers semidouble, vermilion with rose overtones.

'Jean Pabon'—Habit compact; leaves velvetlike; flower clusters large; flowers single, vivid blood red with small white center. An old French cultivar, 1900's.

'La Fiesta'—Flowers large, single, orange scarlet; petals slightly ruffled. Rober, California.

'La Pilote' (erroneous name 'Missouri')— Vigorous; flower clusters large; flowers double, brilliant orange scarlet. Introduced from France in 1889.

'L'Heteranthe' (erroneous names, 'Gen. Grant,' 'Missouri,' 'Michael Buchner)—French type; flowers vivid scarlet. Endures strong sunshine. The original description by S. A. Hill in 1889 notes single and semidouble flowers, and states that this plant was distributed by Lemoine in 1877. A now extinct variety by the name of 'General Grant' was grown in the East and Middle West before 1866, thus antedating the introduction of French types.

'Madame Charles Pomaret'—Plant medium large; flower clusters immense; flowers large, single, deep scarlet. Distinctive.

'Marvel'—Habit tall; leaves velvetlike; flowers medium large, double, brilliant red scarlet, deeper than those of 'Alphonse Ricard.' Originated in Geneva, Ohio, 1886.

'Maryland'—Habit compact; leaves zoned; flowers double, fiery red. Distributed by Vincent Co., Maryland, 1914.

'Michells Sensation'—French type; flowers large, semidouble, luminous scarlet, lighter scarlet on reverse side of petals. Michell, Philadelphia, 1926.

'Montagne Rouge' (more generally called 'Mont Rouge')—Habit large and vigorous; flower clusters very large; flowers single, vivid scarlet. Originated in France, 1880; reintroduced from Canada by The New York Botanical Garden.

'Mrs. William Kent'—Habit small; flowers large, single, red scarlet. Richard Diener, about 1920.

'Olympic Red' ('Alphonse Ricard' × 'Radio Red')—French type; habit large; flower clusters long stalked; flowers large, semidouble, scarlet. Olympia Floral Co., 1939.

'Orient Velvet'—Tall; flower clusters large on very long stalks; flowers very large, single, velvety, deep oriental red. Named for the color by that name in the British Horticultural Colour Chart. Arndt, 1948.

'Paul Crampel'—Habit vigorous, compact; eaves zoned; flowers large, single and semidouble, vermilion red. Lemoine, France, 1892.

'Paul Sloan'—Flower clusters large; flowers large, single, vermilion. England.

'Polly Red' ('Alphonse Ricard' × 'Radio Red')—Habit intermediate; flowers resembling those of 'Alphonse Ricard.' Wilson Bros., Indiana, 1948.

'Pride of Camden (syn. 'Camden Nutt')—Habit compact; flowers double; velvety red. Cannell & Sons, about 1930.

'Radiance'—Flowers large, double, salmon red to vermilion, white at base of petals. Miller, 1950.

'Radio Red'—Habit tall; stems slender; flower clusters on long slender stems; flowers medium large, double, glowing velvety red.

'Red Afterglow'—Flowers medium large, single, blended salmon red and smoky crimson. Miller, 1951.

'Red Barney'—A mutant of 'Madame Barney' from which it differs in having small, double, red flowers.

'Red Landry'—Mutant of 'Madame Landry.' French type; flowers large, semidouble, scarlet with salmon tint.

'Red Robin'—Flowers very large, cherry red with small white center. Arndt, 1948.

'Robers Flame'—Habit vigorous; leaves zoned; flower clusters long-stalked; flowers very large, single, flaming scarlet. Rober, 1940's.

'S. A. Nutt'—Somewhat similar to 'Pride of Camden' but differing in growing slightly larger and in the double, velvety red flowers varying a shade or two in color. Originated in Geneva, Ohio, 1886.

'Scarlet Bedder'—Habit compact; flower clusters not quite as large as those of 'S. A. Nutt'; color of flowers intermediate between 'S. A.

Nutt' and 'Alphonse Ricard.' Introduced by Elmer D. Smith, Adrian, Michigan, 1913.

'Scarlet Tanager'—Habit vigorous; leaves zoned; flowers single, scarlet. Dorcas Brigham, Massachusetts.

'Springfield Vermilion'—Flowers large, two-toned vermilion. California, about 1942.

'Triomphe de Nancy'—Habit compact; leaves zoned; flowers large, double, bright orange scarlet. Introduced from France, 1899.

'Velma'—Vigorous habit of growth; flowers medium large, single, garnet red.

'Wyona'—A mutant of 'Alphonse Ricard' from which it differs in that the flowers are slightly softer in color.

Crimson to Purple Flowers

'Abbie Schaffer'—Small; leaves zoned; flowers double, soft crimson red. Introduced by Hill, Indiana, 1914.

'American Beauty'—Habit of growth rather small; flowers double, cerise crimson. Introduced by Vincent & Son, Maryland, 1915.

'A. M. Mayne' (syn. 'Springfield Violet')—Flowers large, double, rich crimson purple. California, 1942.

'Beauty of Chatsworth' (syns. 'Battle of Gettysburg,' 'California')—Medium large; flowers single, cerise crimson with some scarlet at base of upper petals. Introduced into America, 1912.

'Berkeley Raspberry'—Habit vigorous; flowers large, single, crimson; petals broad and overlapping. Jory, California.

'Better Times'—Habit compact; flowers large, double, crimson with red glow from the center.

'Bougainvillea'—Flowers large, single, purple crimson. Miller, 1945.

'De Quierelle'—Flowers double, purplish crimson, scarlet tints toward base of petals. Introduced by Howard & Smith, 1913.

'Double New Life' (syns. 'Flag of Denmark,' 'Stars and Stripes')—Habit of growth not as bushy as 'New Life' (below); flower clusters smaller and denser; flowers smaller, double; petals narrower and striped red and white. England, 1890.

'Edmond Blanc'—Medium size; leaves lightly zoned; flowers medium large, semidouble, purple, small amount of white at base of petals. Origin obscure.

'El Camino Real'—Flowers double, purplish crimson. California.

'Flora McDonald'—Suggestive of 'Better Times' (above) but the flowers are larger and darker in color. Popular in New England.

'Galli Curci'—Small, compact habit of growth; flowers large, semi-double, purple rose, white at the very base of petals. Rober.

'Gaudy'—Flower clusters large; flowers single, purple-crimson, scarlet at base of upper petals. Miller, 1949.

'Jacquerie'—Medium size; flower clusters fairly large; flowers large, single, crimson with scarlet in the upper petals. Lemoine, 1890's.

'Jean Violette'—Habit compact; flowers medium large, double, purple crimson. A French introduction, grown in America since 1906.

'Lady Mulberry'—Medium large; flower clusters very large; flowers large, single, deep Burgundy red. Arndt, 1948.

'Lady Ruth'—Flowers small, single, purplish crimson with some scarlet in the center. California.

'Ruby' (syns. 'Ruby King,' 'Ruby Queen,' 'New Denver')—Plant medium large; flowers medium large, double, ruby red.

'Magenta Ruby'—Similar to 'Ruby' but the flowers bluer.

'Marquis de Castelane' (syns. 'Lady Jane,' 'My Beauty')—French type; leaves velvetlike as in *P. inquinans*; flowers large, double, rich crimson. Distributed by Bruant and introduced into America about 1901.

'Marquis de Montmart'—Flower clusters large; flowers large, double, magenta crimson with small amount of white at base of petals. Introduced into America with 'Marquis de Castelane.'

'Masures Beauty' (erroneous names, 'American Beauty,' 'Mrs. Smith,' 'Rosalie')—Habit tall, vigorous; flowers large, double, American Beauty red with faint salmon glow. Origin obscure.

'Monsieur Emile David'—French type; flower clusters large, long-stalked; flowers large, double, crimson purple. Handsome, and distinctive for its color, which is deeper and more purple than any others of this class. Originated in France about 1875.

'New Life'—Habit of growth medium large, compact; flowers large, single; petals rounded; the color pattern varying in each flower and sometimes in the individual petals between coral-red and white. Plants in cultivation today closely resemble those illustrated in 1879. Raised by Cannell & Son, England 1877.

'Nuit Poitevine'—Flowers large, single, dark crimson with some dark scarlet in the upper petals. A French form grown in America for more than sixty years. Distinctive for its very dark color.

'Pamela'—Plant medium large; flowers medium large, double, crim- with white center. England, 1900's.

'Suzanne'—Habit compact; leaves darkly zoned; flowers rich purple crimson. Indiana, 1892.

'Virginia Bruce'—Resembles 'Marquis de Castelane' except that there is less blue in the crimson color of the flowers. Rober, 1940's.

'Wicked Lady'—Habit compact; flowers large, single, dark cerise crimson with scarlet at center. Flowers of fine form and distinctive color. Arndt, 1949.

'Will Rogers'—French type; similar to 'Nuit Poitevine' except for very slightly thicker stems.

Carnation-like Flowers

Flowers with toothed petals arise spontaneously from time to time and are not peculiar to the *Pelargonium hortorum* group.

'Cerise Carnation'—Medium size; flowers double, cerise crimson. California.

'Fiat Queen'—A mutant of 'Fiat' from which it differs only in the toothed margins of the petals. Hinsdale, 1941.

'Fringed Poitevine'—A mutant of 'Beauté Poitevine' which it resembles except for the toothed petals. Arndt, 1950.

'Fringed Ricard'—A mutant of 'Alphonse Ricard' distinguished by the toothed petals. Arndt, 1950.

'Jeanne' (a hybrid between cultivars of *P. hortorum* and *P. peltatum*)—Growing habit like that of the garden geranium, small; leaves intermediate in form; flower clusters medium large; flowers small, single, salmon pink; margin of petals toothed.

'Princess Fiat'—A mutant of 'Fiat'; flowers large, double, soft shrimp pink shading to almost white at the toothed margins. California, 1940.

'Sweet William' (erroneous name, 'Mme. Thibaut')—Habit of growth small; stems thick, erect, short; leaves like those of *P. peltatum*; umbels few-flowered; flowers small, single, white, changing to pink as they mature. California.

Rosebud Geraniums

The flowers of this group resemble miniature double roses. The name 'Rosebud' appears in literature back to 1846 but no names mentioned then refer to the following.

'Apple Blossom Rosebud'—Habit compact and bushy; flower clusters medium large; flowers medium large, double, white, rose pink at the margins.

'Crimson Rosebud' (syn. 'Magenta Rosebud')—Similar to the preceding except that the flowers are magenta crimson.

'Pink Rosebud'—Similar to the preceding except that the flowers are pink.

'Red Rosebud'—Similar to the preceding except that the flowers are deep red.

'Salmon Rosebud'—similar to the preceding except that the flowers are salmon pink.

'Scarlet Rosebud'—Similar to the preceding except that the flowers are red scarlet.

Cactus-Flowered Geraniums

The flowers of the following group are characterized by having narrow petals which are sometimes twisted and curled.

'Noel'—Habit compact; flower clusters medium large and composed of fewer individual flowers than the preceding; flowers white, double; petals broader than in the type raised by Mrs. Harvey L. Smith, California, 1948.

'Poinsettia'—Habit of growth medium large, bushy; flower clusters rather dense and globular; flowers double, scarlet; petals narrow, twisted and rolled. Origin obscure.

'Pink Poinsettia'—Habit of growth compact; flowers orchid-pink; petals shorter and broader than those of 'Rosette.'

'Puff'—Habit small, compact; flower clusters medium in size; flowers medium large, semidouble, white; petals narrower than in 'Noel.' Miller, 1948.

'Rosette' (syns. 'Double Poinsettia,' 'Red Poinsettia')—Differs from the preceding in that the stems are more slender; growing habit not as compact; the flowers darker and more red than scarlet. Introduced in California, 1900.

'Silver Star'—Habit compact; flower clusters not as large as in the others; flowers medium large, single, white; petals appear broader than those of 'Puff' because they are less rolled. Miller, 1948.

Bird's-Egg Geraniums

Between 1893 and 1908 a dozen or more geraniums with speckled flowers were imported from France. Similar markings are occasionally found in other bedding geraniums, particularly in ivy geraniums, but none are as uniformly and liberally spotted with pin point dots as the following.

'Baudelaire' (syn. 'Single Pink Bird's-Egg')—Habit of 'Skylark'; flowers single, rose pink, white at the center, crimson dotted. France.

'Curiosa' (syn. 'Double Pink Bird's-Egg')—Habit of growth larger and more vigorous than any of the others; flower stalks very long and strong; flower clusters large and dense; flowers medium large, double, mauve pink; petals carmine dotted. Bruant, 1908.

'J. J. Knight'—Habit of the preceding; flowers single, pale pink, dotted with rose pink. Nebraska, 1947.

'Skylark' (syn. 'Single White Bird's-Egg')—Habit small, compact; flowers single, white, sometimes faintly tinged blush pink; petals heavily spotted with small, rosy carmine dots. France.

Variegated Green and White Leaves

'Attraction'—Habit vigorous, bushy; leaves glistening bright green with ivory border which is narrower and lighter than the border of 'Flower of Spring.'

'Beckwiths Pride'—Habit large, vigorous, bushy; leaves like those of *P. zonale* in shape and texture, bright green, streaked irregularly with creamy white, faintly zoned; flowers medium large, semidouble, soft vermilion. Originated in England about 1900.

'Flower of Spring'—Plant small; stems slender; leaves glistening bright green with a wide, irregular white border; flowers small, single, scarlet. England, 1860.

'Hills of Snow'—Habit of 'Flower of Spring'; leaves similarly thin textured, but the white margins are narrower; flowers small, double, rose pink. Origin obscure.

'Mme. Salleron'—Habit very small, spreading from the base; leaves smaller than any of this group, thin textured, glistening green with an ivory white border; the long petioles distinguish this plant from all others within the group. France, 1845 to 1850. Frequently misspelled 'Mme. Salleroi.'

The preceding plant appears to be of multiple hybrid origin. In the 1850's it was introduced from France to England, where it was known as 'Variegated Dandy.' It mutated freely, giving larger forms, green-leaved forms of straggling habit with stems to three feet long, and forms in which the glistening silver sheen was under the green color instead of over it. Plants identified as 'Mme. Salleron' sometimes appear in cultivation in larger growing form.

'Mountain of Snow'—Habit low, bushy, spreading; leaves thin, shimmering silvery green with wide white margins; flowers small, single, scarlet. Raised by Lenox in England, 1855. A similar variety is listed erroneously as 'Mary Ann.'

'Mrs. Parker'—Habit small, compact; leaves shimmering green, thin, sometimes zoned, medium-wide border of white; flowers small, double, light rose pink. Originated in England. Introduced into America about 1893.

'Silver S. A. Nutt'—A mutant of 'S. A. Nutt' from which it differs only in the leaves which are irregularly bordered and sometimes streaked with ivory white.

'Wilhelm Langgluth' (syn. 'Mrs. Langgluth')—Habit low, spreading; leaves thin, glistening green, margins white; flowers medium large, double, vermilion. Originated in Germany, 1890's. Distinguished by the size and color of the flowers.

Yellow or Golden-Yellow Leaves

'Cloth of Gold'—Habit low growing; leaves golden yellow to greenish yellow; flowers small, single, scarlet. One of the type raised in England, 1860.

'Crystal Palace Gem'—Habit medium large, vigorous, bushy; leaves medium large, light green with irregular blotches and streaks of creamy white to yellow from the green center; flowers small, single, scarlet. A mutant of one of the 'Crystal Palace' series popular in England in the 1850's.

'Dwarf Gold Leaf'—Slightly smaller than 'Cloth of Gold'; leaves similar in color and also zoneless; flowers small, single, bright scarlet. A recurrent form of an early type raised in England during the 1850's.

'Golden Brilliantissima'—Medium large; leaves light green with irregular yellow margins; flowers small, single, scarlet. Raised simultaneously by J. Gibson and H. Park in England, 1873.

'Golden MacMahon'—A mutant of 'Maréchal MacMahon' (described below under "Smooth Bronze-Green Leaves") which it resembles in habit of growth, but differs in that the leaves are yellow and faintly zoned, and develop pink spots when mature; flowers single, light pink. Raised by Philip H. Post, Connecticut.

'Golden Treasure'—Habit of growth larger than most gold-leaved kinds; leaves greenish yellow with rusty orange zone, margins of some leaves tipped bright green at the veins; flowers single, salmon pink. Arndt, 1949.

'Verona'—Habit small, compact; leaves yellow to greenish yellow; flowers small, single, rose pink.

Bright-Colored Leaves (Tricolor Geraniums)

'Carlton Velma'—Habit small, bushy; leaves bright green with golden yellow border, brown zone splashed with mulberry, scarlet, and crimson; flowers single, light salmon. This plant has the most colorful leaves within the group. Arndt, 1948.

'Contrast'—Similar to 'Mrs. Pollock' (below), except that the leaves differ very slightly in shape and coloring, and the color of the flowers varies a shade or two. California.

'Display'—Habit small, compact; leaves fairly large, partly green, the brown zone splashed with scarlet and crimson, margins yellow, scalloped; flowers small, single, scarlet. Miller, 1949.

'Fairyland'—Dwarf habit of growth; leaves small, dark gray green with wide ivory white margins, zoned with irregular splashes of rose red; flowers small, single, light scarlet. Miller, 1951.

'Filigree'—Plant low and bushy; leaves interestingly lobed, silvery green with wide creamy white border, lightly zoned with pink and brown; flowers small, single, deep salmon. Miller, 1953.

'Happy Thought'—Habit medium large, bushy, vigorous; leaves bright green with a large yellow to creamy yellow butterfly in the center, faintly zoned with splashes of brown and orange; flowers small, single, vermilion. A mutant raised by Lynes in Warwick, England, 1877. An earlier plant by this name was developed by Peter Grieve and differs in that the colors are reversed—the outer part of the leaves is yellow and the butterfly in the center is green.

'Jane Maxwell'—Leaves fairly large, flat and crenately lobed, color values similar to those of 'Skies of Italy' but the difference in the size and shape of the leaves makes them appear more colorful; flowers single, red. Connecticut, 1946.

'Lady Cullum'—Habit small, bushy; leaves green edged with creamy yellow, the zone splashed with crimson and red but not as brightly as in other geraniums of this class; flowers single, dull red. Developed by Peter Grieve in England, 1860. A lilac-pink flowered form was grown in 1866.

'Maximilian'—Habit small, bushy; leaves bright green with yellow border, brown zone splashed with crimson and scarlet, and only slightly less brilliant than 'Carlton Velma'; distinctive for its double salmon orange flowers. Introduced from Mexico by M. H. Arndt in the 1940's.

'Miss Burdett Coutts'—Differs from all others in that the leaves are overlaid with a silvery film; center green, wide margins ivory-white, the zone splashed brown and rosy red; flowers small, single, scarlet. Peter Grieve, 1860.

'Mrs. Cox'—Medium size; leaves velvety green with narrow yellow border, brown zone splashed with scarlet and crimson; flowers small, single, pale salmon. England, 1923.

'Mrs. Pollock'—Habit medium large, vigorous, bushy; leaves medium large, green with yellow margins, red and crimson break from the broad brown zone; flowers medium large, single, scarlet. Peter Grieve, England, 1858. There is also a double flowered form.

'Pastel'—Habit medium large; leaves silvery green with wide ivory border, wide zone of coral pink splashed with purplish brown; flowers single, salmon pink to coral pink matching the zone color of the leaves. Miller, 1954.

'Pink Happy Thought'—Similar to 'Happy Thought' except that the flowers are rose pink.

'Skies of Italy'—Habit small, bushy; leaves green with pointed lobes and creamy yellow margins, zone intense brown splashed with scarlet, orange scarlet, and crimson; flowers small, single, scarlet.

Smooth Bronze-Green Leaves

'Alpha' (syn. 'Dakota')—A French hybrid of *P. peltatum* and a bronze-leaved *P. hortorum* cultivar. Habit of growth small, bushy; stems slender; leaves small, glossy, yellow green with a narrow rust red border; flowers small, single, scarlet. Introduced into America in 1912.

'Bismarck'—Habit compact; leaves medium large, yellow green with a bright rust red zone, margins scalloped; flowers small, single, light salmon pink. Introduced 1875.

'Bronze Beauty'—Slow growing; leaves large, yellow green with a comparatively narrow reddish brown zone; flowers small, single, light salmon pink.

'Distinction' (syn. 'One-in-a-Ring')—Habit small, spreading; leaves roundish, heart-shaped at base, light green with a very narrow well defined brown-black zone close to the edge, margins toothed and crinkled; flowers small, single, cherry red. Originated in England and grown in America since 1879.

'Jubilee'—Habit tall, vigorous; leaves yellow green with a very broad rust red to bronze brown zone; flowers small, single, light salmon pink. Introduced into America from England about 1890.

'Maréchal MacMahon'—Habit medium, bushy; leaves yellow green with a rust red to bronze brown zone well in from the margins; flowers small, single, scarlet. Originated in France about 1862 and named for one of Napoleon's generals.

'Roderick Dhu'—Habit of growth similar to 'Maréchal MacMahon'; leaves similar except that the zone is not as broad or as distinct; flowers small, single, light salmon pink.

'Scarlet Bronze Beauty'—Similar to 'Bronze Beauty' in habit of growth; the leaves differ in having a bright rust red zone and scalloped margins; flowers small, single, scarlet.

Velvetlike Bronze-Green Leaves

'Black Diamond'—Plant medium large; leaves medium large, velvety green with very broad zone of blue grape purple, green center and margins become lightly overlaid with the zone color as the leaves become older, undersurfaces mellow wine red with prominent light green veins; flowers medium large, single, salmon, paling toward center. Arndt, 1950.

'Esmeranda'—Very tall; stems slender, branching, succulent, becoming woody; stems and branches soft-hairy when young; leaves to two and one-half inches or more and similar to those of *P. inquinans* in shape and texture, young leaves almost emerald green with bronze green in the center and bronze green zone, mature leaves bronze green with a darker bronze center; flowers single, murky salmon pink; upper petals broader and widely separated from the lower ones. Apparently a hybrid which escaped from cultivation and was found clambering over shrubs and trees to a length of thirty feet. Introduced from Mexico by M. H. Arndt.

'Green Maximilian'—Habit medium large, bushy; leaves bright velvety green with dark bronze brown zone; flowers double, vermilion. Arndt, 1949.

'Russet'—Habit of growth medium tall, vigorous; stems thicker than those of 'Esmeranda'; leaves larger, similar in shape, basal lobes overlapping, green in center with chocolate-brown zone, narrow margins of light bronze green, and the whole overlaid with rosy bronze; flower clusters large for the type, flowers medium large, single, rusty salmon pink. Distinctive. Arndt, 1949.

'Rusty Fire'—Similar to the preceding in habit of growth and color of leaves; flower clusters large, flowers single, medium large, bright scarlet. Distinctive. Arndt, 1949.

Dwarf Geraniums

'Alabaster Star'—Grows to six inches tall, bushy; leaves light green, about an inch and a half in diameter; flower clusters large; flowers large, single, white. Arndt, 1952.

'Black Vesuvius'—To eight inches tall; leaves small—to an inch, very dark green with a barely visible black-green zone; flowers conspicuously large for so small a plant, single, orange scarlet. England, 1889.

'Brilliant Star'—Similar to 'Alabaster Star' in habit of growth and size; leaves green with medium-wide black zone; flowers large, single, fiery red scarlet. Produces an abundance of flower clusters that appear to envelop the whole plant. Arndt, 1952.

'Brooks Barnes'—Habit of growth similar to 'Alabaster Star'; leaves rounded, small, purple black, veins depressed; flowers single, medium large, salmon deepening toward the center. Arndt, 1952.

'Imp'—Similar to 'Black Vesuvius' in habit of growth and size, and in coloring of the leaves; flowers large, single, salmon pink. Raised by H. C. Miller, California, 1950.

'Kleiner Liebling' (translation, 'Little Darling')—To eight inches tall, spreading; leaves to an inch or slightly more, fresh bright green; flowers large, single, bright rose pink. Originated in Germany, 1925.

'Mischief'—Growing habit small; leaves small, dark olive to black green; flower clusters small; flowers small, orange scarlet; petals narrow, curled and twisted. Intermediate in size between dwarf and small growing garden geraniums. Miller, 1951.

'Madame Fournier' (syn. 'Scarlet Pimpernel')—To eight inches tall; leaves small, dark purplish green to black green with darker zone; flowers small, single, scarlet. An old French cultivar.

'Pigmy'—Similar in habit to 'Mme. Fournier'; leaves light green, zoned; flowers small, double, red. (Not related to Lemoine's 'Pygmée.') Origin obscure.

'Pixie'—To eight inches tall, bushy; leaves dark olive green to purplish green, darker zoned; flowers small, single, pale salmon. Miller, California, 1947.

'Sprite'—To eight inches tall; leaves gray green with a wide ivory white border; flowers small, single, salmon coral. Miller, 1949.

'Yellow Star'—Similar to 'Alabaster Star' in habit of growth; leaves medium green, zoned, with narrow margins of golden yellow; flower clusters large; flowers large, single, rosy tangerine. Arndt, 1952.

Distinctive New Miniatures

The following pelargoniums have been selected from among five hundred new dwarf hybrids developed by Mr. Milton H. Arndt from 1949 to 1950. The sizes of these range from one to eight inches in height after more than a year of growth. The color and form of the leaves vary considerably; the leaves of some kinds are more deeply scalloped than others, and in many plants the veins are depressed, giving the leaves a fluted appearance; some have ruffled margins; a very few have leaves with flat surfaces. Included also are dwarfs with golden, white, and colored leaves.

'Artemis'—Bushy, to six inches tall; leaves green with brown-purple zone, many edged with soft rose red; flowers medium size, double, rose pink shaded with white.

'Blanco'—To six inches tall, bushy; densely branching; leaves to about an inch, green, margins ruffled, basal lobes overlapping; flowers small, semidouble, pure white.

'Brownie'—To four inches tall, bushy; leaves small—to an inch, green with purple-black zone and purple haze over green; flower clusters large; flowers large, single, scarlet.

'Carlton Pet'—To four inches tall, bushy; leaves to an inch, green, with purple-black zone; flowers medium large, single, white in center surrounded by salmon, salmon-veined white toward margins.

'Chit'—To eight inches tall, bushy; leaves to a little more than an inch, flat surfaced, green, deeply scalloped; flowers large, single, vivid scarlet.

'Doc'—To four inches tall, bushy; leaves to an inch, light green, zoneless, margins scalloped and ruffled; flowers semidouble, deep red.

'Dopey'—Height to two and one-half inches, compact; leaves to a half inch; dark green overcast with purple, shallowly scalloped; flowers small, single, bright cerise pink.

'Elf'—To four inches tall; leaves to more than an inch, green, zoneless, the margins conspicuously scalloped; flowers large, single, velvety dark scarlet; petals rounded.

'Fairy'—To three inches tall, bushy; leaves to an inch, medium green with conspicuous purple-black zone, margins ruffled; flowers single, salmon-pink.

'Genie'—To four inches tall; leaves to an inch, bright green, narrow purple-black zone; flowers single, scarlet.

'Gnome'—To four inches tall; leaves to an inch, dark plum-purple zone on green, overcast with a glow of the zone color, margins of leaves ruffled; flowers single, light salmon red.

'Gulliver'—To eight inches tall; densely branching; leaves to an inch or more, bright green with purple-black zone; flowers large, single, bright scarlet with white eye. Floriferous.

'Kiffa'—Bushy, to six inches tall; leaves to one and a half inches, bright green, faintly zoned; flowers double, pale salmon pink.

'Lilliput'—To four inches tall; leaves to an inch, green, ruffled; flowers small, fiery red with white eye; petals overlapping.

'Mars'—Bushy, to six inches tall; leaves to an inch and a half, blue green, dark zoned; flowers double, deep crimson.

'Meteor'—Bushy, to six inches tall; leaves green, the margins pointedly scalloped; florets in dense clusters, double, crimson. Lighter in leaf and flower than 'Mars.'

'Minikin'—To five inches tall, bushy; leaves to an inch or slightly more, green, the zone purple black, basal lobes overlapping, margins ruffled; flowers medium large, single; upper petals white, salmon veined; lower petals salmon paling to white at base and edges.

'Nixie'—To four inches tall; leaves to an inch, green; flowers very large, single, salmon red.

'Peri'—To six inches tall; densely branching; leaves to an inch, green, deeply scalloped; flowers large, single, bright scarlet.

'Puck'—To five inches tall, bushy; leaves to an inch or slightly more, velvety green with broad wine purple zone close to the margins; flowers large, single, pale salmon.

'Rosy Dawn'—Bushy, to six inches tall; leaves green with medium dark zone; flowers double, rosy orange. Distinctive flower color.

'Sheratan'—Bushy, to six inches tall; leaves green with medium dark zone; flowers double, raspberry red.

'Sleepy'—To two inches tall; leaves to a half inch, bright olive-green with blue-purple zone; flowers small, single, light salmon pink with paler margins.

'Sneezie'—To four inches tall, bushy; leaves to three-quarters inch, dark green, lightly zoned purple, the margins scalloped; flowers single to semidouble, flesh pink.

'Snow White'—To six inches tall, bushy; leaves to three-quarters inch, bright green with faint narrow zone; flowers semidouble, pure white with conspicuous golden stamens.

'Tiny'—To four inches tall, bushy; leaves to about an inch, bright green with faint darker green zone, the margins scalloped; flowers single, salmon red.

'Tiny Pat'—To six inches tall, bushy and branching; leaves green, faintly zoned, deeply scalloped; flower clusters large; flowers large, single, pink; lower petals white half way from center to base. This miniature has the largest flowers within this group and they resemble those of 'Patricia Audette' (page 40).

'Tiny Tim'—One inch tall, bushy; leaves one-quarter inch, dark purple green with black zone; thirty-five leaves can compose a bushy mound one inch tall and an inch and a half in diameter; tiny flowers of deep salmon.

'Tomtit'—To eight inches tall; densely branching; leaves to an inch or more, green, narrow purple-black zone, the teeth at margins tipped with purple black; flowers medium large, single, scarlet.

'Vega'—Bushy, to four inches tall; leaves to about an inch and somewhat smaller than than those of 'Sheratan', green with brown green zone; flowers single; upper petals creamy white and pale pink veined at the base; lower petals pure white, faintly suffused with pink and pink veined at the base.

Dwarfs with Colored Leaves

'Bashful'—To four inches tall; leaves to three-quarters inch, creamy white with irregular small green blotch in center; flowers large, single, bright orange red. Must be grown in the shade as it cannot withstand direct sunshine. Arndt.

'Elfin'—Habit dwarf; leaves small, dark gray green with wide yellow border, zoned with irregular splashes of red; flowers small, single, scarlet. Miller, 1952.

'Golden Finch'—To four inches tall; leaves to an inch, golden yellow, the margins deeply scalloped; flowers single, orange scarlet. Arndt.

'Golden Oriole'—To six inches tall; leaves to an inch or more, light yellow green, broad pale pinkish rust zone, margins irregularly scalloped; flowers single, salmon scarlet. Arndt.

'Grumpy'—To four inches tall; leaves three-quarters inch, gold or lemon yellow, depending upon light conditions, pale pink to red zone; flowers single, orange scarlet. Arndt.

'Happy'—To four inches tall, bushy; leaves to an inch, long-petioled, bright gold, broad rust-red zone, the margins scalloped; flower clusters long-stalked; flowers soft salmon pink. Arndt.

'Little Diamond'—A dwarf form of 'Black Diamond'; undersurfaces of leaves red; good-sized clusters of single scarlet flowers. Arndt, 1951.

'Whitecap'—Plants dwarf; leaves olive green, zoneless; flowers medium size, single, white, in large clusters; margins of petals waved. Miller, 1952.

'White Lady'—('Carlton Velma' × 'Miss Burdett Coutts'). To eight inches tall, bushy; leaves small, white with a small dark green butterfly in the center, a narrow pale pink zone surrounding butterfly like a halo; flowers large, single, bright salmon red. Arndt.

New Large Forms with Colored Leaves

'Carlton Glory'—Large; leaves orbicular and overlapping at base, shallowly scalloped, lightly zoned; flower clusters large; flowers very large, to more than two and a half inches, single orbicular, velvety Chinese red. Arndt, 1954.

'Carlton Glory Pink'—Similar to 'Carlton Glory' except that the leaves are lighter green, and the shaded soft pink flowers have a white center. Arndt, 1954.

'Carlton Glory Salmon'—Similar to 'Carlton Glory Pink' except that flowers are shaded soft salmon. Arndt, 1954.

'Carrousel'—Habit of growth medium large; leaves medium large, green with broad zone of purple and rose pink, marked with white sections like spokes of a wheel from center to margins; flowers large, single, salmon. Arndt, 1954.

'Don Quixote'—Plant medium large; leaves medium large, white with large irregular patches and segments of green; broad pale pink zone; flowers large, single, bright salmon rose. Arndt, 1954.

'Emma Thacher'—Habit of growth medium large, bushy; leaves large, velvety, green, the center splashed pale yellow and light green, a broad zone of raspberry-red slightly splashed with purple, the margins pale yellow; flowers medium large, single, bright salmon. Differs from 'Carlton Velma' in that the leaves are more velvety, the yellow margins wider, and there are fewer purple splashes in the zone. Arndt, 1952.

'Natalie Webster'—Habit of growth medium large, bushy; young leaves bright green with broad wine purple zone, green area of mature leaves overcast with wine purple; flowers single, salmon pink paling toward margins of petals, conspicuous white eye in center, petals rounded. Arndt, 1952.

'Pink Hydrangea'—Large growing; leaves bright green, lightly zoned, pointed at the tip, deeply scalloped and coarsely toothed, ruffled; flower clusters very large on long stalks; flowers very large, semidouble, bright pink. Remotely suggests a globular vivid rose pink hydrangea flower cluster. Arndt, 1954.

'Polychrome'—Plant medium large; leaves medium large, light golden yellow with large, irregular pie-shaped sections of green, and with a bright salmon-pink zone; flowers large, single bright salmon rose.

'Polyverde'—Medium large; leaves medium large, white with large gray green and green butterfly, broadly light pink zoned; flowers large, single, salmon.

'Red Spider'—Habit of growth medium large, bushy; leaves velvety bright green, faintly zoned, bright red veined; flowers single, medium large, scarlet. A new cultivar distinctive because of the unusual red veining in the leaves. Arndt, 1952.

'Rusty Max'—Medium large; leaves medium large, fresh bright green center and margins, cocoa-brown zone splashed with light green; flowers large, single, scarlet, white at base of petals. Mutant of 'Maximilian.'

'White Camellia'—Medium large; leaves bright green, lightly zoned; flower clusters large, long-stalked; flowers large, double, white; flower buds green tinged. Arndt, 1954.

Chapter 2

PELARGONIUM PELTATUM

Ivy geraniums are abundantly grown in California and are a delight to all who visit there. Regrettably they are not so frequently planted in the East, though they can be grown satisfactorily there also. They thrive in sunny locations in any reasonably good soil.

Their uses in California are utilitarian as well as ornamental. In place of grass for bordering sidewalks, ivy geraniums there make colorful ground covers. Banks and terraces glow with their showy flower clusters. The plants also trail from walls, window boxes, and urns.

These vinelike pelargoniums are descended from *P. peltatum,* and they follow this parent species in their trailing habit of growth. Their stems may extend from three to ten feet or more, their length depending on the variety, the environment, or both. Where the plants can live outdoors the year around the stems and branches become noticeably woody.

The leaves are mostly glossy in surface finish and succulent in texture. Their angular lobes give them roughly the appearance of English ivy leaves.

Flower colors approximate those of the garden geraniums (the *P. hortorum* group), with the added distinctions of more brightly colored veins and feathering or other ornamentation on the petals. The flower clusters are looser; these and the slender arching flower stalks combine to give a graceful and airy appearance as they protrude beyond the foliage.

BACKGROUND OF THE GROUP

Before 1860 the history of the ivy geranium is not clear. It has never had the attention that hybridizers gave to *P. domesticum* and *P. hortorum*, although *P. peltatum* has been cultivated since 1701 and the similar species *P. lateripes,* since the 1780's. A plant supposed to be a hybrid between these two species was called *P. pinguifolium* by Sweet. Others were described as species but have since been considered wild varieties of *P. peltatum,* which appears to vary in its pubescence and in the zoning of the leaves.

Literature reveals that extensive hybridizing of *P. peltatum* with forms of what we now know as *P. hortorum* began in England about 1860. It is recorded that in 1872 a *P. peltatum* "variety" crossed with a bronze-leaved geranium covered a 15 × 9-foot wall; in 1874 a hybrid of similar parentage is described as having "blue" (probably purple) flowers.

It is reasonable to assume that in the eager pursuit of crossing vine-like geraniums with garden bedding geraniums, the offspring was distributed as a variant of one or the other parent, depending upon which it resembled in habit of growth. It is noteworthy that the dominant characters of the ivy geranium prevail in our so-called *P. peltatum* cultivars, even though we know, or at least sometimes suspect, that many or most of them are derived in part from the garden geranium. Among the earliest English ivy geraniums still in cultivation are 'Leopard' from the 1870's; 'Galilee,' 1882; 'Mrs. Hawley' and 'Ryecroft Surprise,' from the 1890's. Those of French origin include 'L'Elégante' (syn. 'Sunset'), the 1870's; 'Jeanne d'Arc,' which more closely resembles the species in flower than any other, 1870's; 'Gringoire,' 1890's, and 'L'Etincelant' (syn. 'Intensity *'), 1870's.

Vinelike pelargoniums with shorter stems and more intensely colored flowers had their accidental origin in a *P. peltatum* "variety" crossed with *P. hortorum* in the greenhouses of Lemoine about 1895. Examples of this type are 'César Franck' and 'Charles Monselet.' A similar origin is even more evident in 'Sweet William' (miscalled

* A better translation would be 'Sparkle' or 'The Sparkler.'

'Mme. Thibaut'). The stems of these plants are more erect than those of most other hybrids of this class. Another group of similar ancestry but more like *P. hortorum* in character includes 'Alliance' (syn. 'Victory'), with arching stems, 'Cordens Glory' (syns. 'Gordons Glory,' 'Scarlet Glory').

In the *P. hortorum* group there are plants which occasionally produce lax or arching stems. These are probably hybrids of an earlier period which are now reverting, thereby showing belatedly a relationship to *P. peltatum.*

MODERN IVY GERANIUMS

Flower colors of today's ivy geraniums approximate those of the garden geranium group, *P. hortorum.* They have the added distinction, however, of brighter-colored veins with occasional feathering and other ornamentation on the petals.

Trailing geraniums are exceedingly showy and floriferous plants for window-boxes, tubs, urns, trellises, and hanging containers. They are admirably suited also for hillsides, banks, and retaining walls (when they are planted at the top), and as ground covers either on level areas or on slopes. In Latin American countries they are often used as wall covers in patios or outside. Where necessary, long-stemmed kinds may be kept within bounds by pinching off the new growth at the tip.

Even in regions where the outdoor culture of geraniums must be seasonal, stems up to six feet in length are often attainable. In climates where outdoor growing can be practiced through the year, *P. peltatum* types will trail or spread to twelve feet or more.

The rather remarkable weather tolerance of ivy geraniums was evidenced one summer on Long Beach Island off the New Jersey coast where strong winds prevail. Planted late in May in window boxes exposed to the south, two medium-long-stemmed plants spread over each window box and trailed a foot below by early August. A succession of flower clusters developed from late June until salt spray from a September "northeaster" blighted the flowers and most of the leaves. The plants recovered, however, after being removed to a sheltered location.

The group of ivy geraniums comprises fewer cultivars than the

P. hortorum group. Those selected for description below are considered the choicest by many growers. The species itself and one very closely related are first described.

P. peltatum (L.) L'Hér. ex Ait.—Stems succulent-woody, smooth, to six feet long or more, trailing, branching; leaves succulent, glossy, light green and sometimes dark-zoned, angularly five-lobed and shield-shape with the petiole inserted slightly inside the margin of the blade, roughly resembling those of the English ivy (*Hedera helix*) in outline; umbels axillary or opposite the leaves, extending beyond the foliage, usually five- to eight-flowered, the flowers with a slender spur twice as long as the sepals or more, the petals nearly equal, white or pink, the upper two broader and strongly veined and spotted with carmine. Native in South Africa, introduced into England in 1701. Illustrated in Curtis's Botanical Magazine t. 20 (1787) and by Andrews, *Geraniums* t. 44 as *Geranium peltatum* and by Sweet, t. 95, as *P. scutatum*. The closest approach to the flower form of the species among cultivated clones may be seen in 'Jeanne d'Arc.'

P. lateripes L'Hér. ex Ait.—Habit of growth similar to that of *P. peltatum* from which it differs in that the petiole is attached at the heart-shaped base of the blade, and the leaf margins are slightly toothed. A South African species introduced into England in the 1780's. Illustrated by L'Héritier, *Geraniologia*, t. 24, and by Andrews, *Geraniums*, t. 38, but under the name *Geranium hederinum*. A plant very similar to *P. lateripes* was illustrated by Sweet, t. 52, as *P. pinguifolium*. Sweet thought that it might represent a hybrid between *P. lateripes* and *P. peltatum*, but for practical purposes it is not easy to distinguish from *P. lateripes*.

SELECTED CULTIVARS OF PELARGONIUM PELTATUM

(Ivy Geraniums)

'Achievement' (*P. hortorum* × *P. peltatum*)—Vigorous; stems medium long; flower clusters large; flowers large, semidouble, soft cerise pink, brighter marking in upper petals. Vincent, Maryland, 1910.

'Admiral Byrd' (syn. 'Orchid Triumph')—Stems long; flowers large, semidouble, lilac pink, cerise marking in upper petals. California.

'Alba Plena'—Stems medium long; flowers small, semidouble, pure

white with no marking. Distinct from all others of this class because
of a rounded solid green core about the size of a pea in the center
of the flower. California, about 1948.

'Bridesmaid'—Stems long; flowers large, double, soft orchid pink.
Schmidt, 1942.

'Butterflies'—Stems long; flowers large, single, lavender with deeper
overtones, red marking in upper petals. Schmidt, 1948.

'César Franck'—Stems medium long; flowers medium large, semidouble, brilliant rose red with orange overtones. Distributed by Vincent, 1914.

'Carlos Uhden'—Stems medium long; flowers large, double, cerise
rose shading to white at center. Distributed by Howard & Smith, 1913.

'Carnival'—Flowers large, double, mauve pink with a distinctive,
large, carmine blotch in the upper petals. Schmidt, 1950.

'Cayucas'—stems medium long; flowers large, double, rose pink with
violet tones, dark violet veins and cerise spot in upper petals. Rober,
California.

'Charles Monselet'—Stems medium long; flowers large, double, brilliant cerise rose red. Introduced from France about 1900.

'Cliff House'—Stems medium long; flowers medium large, double,
pale orchid. Rober.

'Colonel Baden-Powell'—Stems medium long; flowers large, semidouble, white tinged with lavender, cerise marking in upper petals.
England, 1900.

'Comtesse de Grey'—Stems long; flowers medium large, semidouble,
soft pink with pale violet marking in upper petals.

'Dieners Lavender' (syns. 'Lavender Giant,' 'Giant Lavender')—Vigorous; stems long; flowers very large, semidouble, pale lavender. Richard Diener, California, 1930's.

'El Gaucho'—Flowers large, double, bright rose cerise with light
violet undertone, base of upper petals marked crimson. Schmidt, 1951.

'Emily Sylvia'—Flowers medium large, single, showing a tendency
to double because of the very small curled petals in the center, bright
rose red with an orange tinge in the center. California.

'Estelle Doheny'—Similar to 'Souvenir de Charles Turner' except
that the double rose pink flowers are tinged with salmon. California.

'Galilee'—Stems medium long; flowers medium large, double, clear
rose pink. England, 1882.

'Gringoire'—Stems medium long; flowers large, double, satiny rose carmine. France, 1890's.

'Jeanne d'Arc'—Stems long; flowers large, single, white suffused with palest lavender, reddish streaks in upper petals. Lemoine, 1870's. The flowers of this ivy geranium resemble those of the species more closely in form than any others known to me.

'Jester' [(*P. peltatum* × 'Queen Alexandra') × ('Colonel Baden-Powell' × 'Dieners Lavender')]—Stems medium long; flowers large, double, orchid pink; petals rose flecked at the margins; occasional flowers in a cluster may be all rose pink or rose red. Schmidt, 1942.

'Joseph Warren'—Stems medium long; flowers large, double, rose purple. England. Distinctive for its vivid purple flowers.

'Judy'—Stems short; flower clusters unusually large; flowers large, semidouble, cerise rose. California.

'Lavender Gem'—Stems medium to long; leaves darker than usual; flowers medium large, double, pale lavender.

'Lavender Rose'—Stems medium long; leaves dark green; flowers double, pale lavender.

'L'Elégante' (syn. 'Sunset')—Stems medium long; leaves green with irregular margins of creamy white sometimes pink tinged; flowers small, single, pale pink. Originated in France, exhibited in England in 1866, and introduced into America, 1877.

'Leopard'—Stems rather short; flowers large, semidouble, orchid pink, petals cerise spotted, upper petals veined cerise. England, 1870's.

'L'Etincelant' (syns. 'Intensity,' 'Red Majesty')—Stems long; flowers large, semidouble, intense scarlet. Introduced from France, 1913.

'Lucky Strike'—Stems medium long; flowers medium large, double, deep rose pink, red marked at base of upper petals. Schmidt, 1946.

'Madame Margot'—Stems medium long; leaves variegated green and creamy white; flowers medium large, single, satiny white, faintly lilac tinged.

'Louise Thibaut' (erroneous name, 'Madame Thibaut')—Habit of *P. peltatum*; stems medium long; flowers large, double, "resembling small roses," bright rose pink with salmon tinge. France, 1882.

'Modesto'—Stems medium long; flowers large, double, shading from cerise rose to pink with orange glint in center. Rober.

'Mrs. Banks'—Stems long; flowers medium large, semidouble, bluish white marked with pale violet in upper petals. England, 1908.

'Mrs. Hawley' (syn. 'Double Violet Cerise')—Stems medium to long; flowers large, double, cerise with violet overtones. England, 1899.

'Mrs. H. J. Jones'—Stems long; flowers medium large, double, deep rose pink with salmon overtones; margins of petals toothed. Developed by H. J. Jones at Ryecroft Nursery, England, 1900.

'Neon'—Stems long; flowers large, double, cerise rose with violet undertones. Schmidt, 1942.

'Old Mexico'—Flower clusters large, flowers medium large, semi-double, rose cerise with less violet than 'Neon,' deep maroon stripes at base of upper petals. Schmidt, 1948.

'Princess Victoria'—Stems medium to long; flowers medium large, double, pale violet. Imported from England in 1906.

'Queen Alexandra' (syns. 'Princess Victoria,' 'La France,' 'Enchantress')—Stems medium long; flowers large, double, white to blush, each petal flecked rose pink at the margins. Imported from England, 1906.

'Rose Enchantress'—A mutant of the preceding from which it differs in having bright orchid pink flowers with crimson spots in all petals.

'Ryecroft Surprise'—Stems medium long; flowers similar to those of 'Comtesse de Grey' but differing in being larger and brighter soft pink. Originated at Ryecroft Nursery, England, and imported by Dreer & Co., Philadelphia, 1901.

'Salmon'—Stems long; flowers large, semidouble, rose pink salmon with reddish veins at base of upper petals.

'Salmon Enchantress'—A mutant of 'Queen Alexandra' which it resembles except that the flowers are soft pink, flecked and striped with rose pink at the margins of petals.

'Salmon King'—Stems long; flowers large, double, pink with salmon tinge.

'San José Peru'—Stems long, slender; flowers very large, semidouble, cerise rose upon opening and maturing to velvetlike smoky vermilion blended with rose red, and with purple stripes from center to base of upper petals. Distinctive in color. Introduced from Mexico by Arndt, 1949.

'Silesia'—Stems medium long; flowers medium large, single, cerise rose with faint violet undertone, dark spot in upper petals and dark veined at the base. California.

'Snowdrift' (syn. 'Double White')—Stems medium long, slender; flowers medium large, double, white, blush pink at base of petals.

'Souvenir de Charles Turner' (syn. 'Charles Turner')—Stems long; growth vigorous; flowers large, double, vivid rose pink. France, 1880's.

'Sybil Holmes'—Stems medium long; flowers large, double, deep silvery pink, underside of petals paler. Rober, 1940's.

'The Blush'—Similar to 'Sybil Holmes' except that the flowers are lighter in color and the reverse of petals almost white. Introduced by Howard & Smith, 1913. Originated in England, 1890.

'The Duchess'—Stems medium long; flowers semidouble, white faintly orchid flushed, short pink lines at veins of petal margins. Schmidt, 1948.

'Valencia'—Flowers large, semidouble, deep pink, upper petals marked with white bar, crimson stripes and round spot. Schmidt, 1951.

'Willy' (syns. 'Berkeley Red,' 'Dark Red,' 'Incomparable')—Stems medium long; flowers large, double, deep red.

SCANDENT TYPES VISIBLY INFLUENCED BY P. HORTORUM

'Alliance' (syn. 'Victory')—Vigorous; stems thick, arching or lax; zoned leaves like those of the garden geranium in texture, the lobing variable; flower clusters like those of *P. hortorum* in form; flowers long-stalked, large, double, lilac white with deep rose pink markings. Lemoine, France.

'Cordens Glory' (syns. 'Gordons Glory,' 'Scarlet Beauty,' 'Scarlet Glory')—Stems short, thick, lax, but rarely drooping; flowers medium large, semidouble, brilliant red with lighter streaks in some of the upper petals. Plants propagated by cuttings sometimes produce erect stems. England, 1890's.

'Pink Alliance'—Similar to 'Alliance,' from which it differs in that the flowers are deep pink and the reverse of petals blush pink.

GARDEN GERANIUMS INFLUENCED BY P. PELTATUM

'Aztec'—Habit of *P. hortorum*; stems erect, occasionally lax; flower clusters large; flowers medium large, semidouble, deep vermilion with light bronze overtones. Miller, 1947.

'E. H. Trego'—Frequently confused with 'Louise' which has salmon rose pink flowers, is without trace of *P. peltatum* influence, and apparently not in cultivation. Some stems are said to show a tendency to trail; flowers large, double, intense scarlet. Introduced about 1914.

'Irma'—General habit of *P. hortorum*; some stems lax; leaves small; flowers double, salmon apricot, white at base of petals. California, 1939.

'Julia B. Cornelis'—Mutant of 'Jeanne.' Medium large in habit of growth; stems slender, tending to trail; leaves show less of *P. peltatum* than those of 'Jeanne'; flower clusters medium large; flowers medium large, single, soft coral vermilion. Arose at the Coolkenny Nursery.

'Lullaby' ('Emile Zola' × 'Irma')—Stems erect; flowers medium large, double, salmon apricot, lacking the white at base of petals. Miller, 1948.

'Milky Way'—Habit of *P. hortorum* but an occasional stem lax; flowers large, semidouble, white with pale orchid tint. California, about 1946.

'Ramona'—Habit of *P. hortorum* but an occasional stem lax; flowers large, double, blended vermilion, crimson, and rose. California.

Chapter 3

PELARGONIUM DOMESTICUM

It is a curious thing that while the bedding geranium has always been known as a geranium, the even more showy group which is characterized by the Martha Washington type has come to be known as a pelargonium. In the past this assemblage, which is of multiple hybrid origin, has been called at various times by such names as "Show" pelargoniums and "Grandiflorums" in England, "Edel" (Regal) pelargoniums in Germany, and until recently in North America, "Martha Washington" or "Lady Washington" pelargoniums. In 1901, L. H. Bailey devised the technical name *Pelargonium domesticum* for these pelargoniums and it is by this name that they are frequently known today.

PARENTAGE AND EARLY HYBRIDIZING

The origin of *P. domesticum* is obscure. Certainly among the first parents were *P. cucullatum, P. angulosum, P. cordifolium* and later *P. acerifolium* and *P. betulinum* from which the shrubby habit, general leaf shape, and quantity of flowers were derived. *P. grandiflorum* is thought to have been responsible for good form and size in the flowers and *P. fulgidum* has contributed bright color. According to some horticultural writers as many as twenty species in pure or hybrid form have been involved in the development of *P. domesticum* as we know its members today.

77

Between 1815 and 1830 there was a great deal of hybridizing on the part of a number of amateur and professional growers, particularly in Chelsea, England. During these years the desirable qualities of what came to be known as *P. domesticum* began to take shape so that in his fifth volume, Sweet was able to illustrate the forerunners of today's plants. At the same time similar hybrids produced in Germany were being illustrated by Leopold Trattinnick in a series of volumes supplementing those of Sweet.

The next major improvements were noted in the developments of Hoyle and Foster around the middle of the nineteenth century. About 1860 intensive hybridizing was undertaken to produce larger flowers; it is recorded that during this period five generations of crosses were made between *P. grandiflorum* and *P. glaucum*. The large-flowered descendants of these crosses are evident in cultivars that are still in favor; to mention a few: 'Mary Elizabeth,' 1870; 'Mrs. Harrison,' 1873; 'Maid of Kent' (erroneous name, 'Duchess of Kent'), 1873; 'Mabel,' 1879.

In Germany, a man named Richter pioneered in the production of more colorful flowers. He began hybridizing in 1880, and in 1896 exhibited forty-five new shades at the Spring Fair in Dresden. Carl Faiss, and F. W. Burger, and a Mr. Bornemann, among others, followed Richter in contributing other colors and shades. Many of these plants were shipped to America and today they are standard cultivars here. These imported plants have provided numerous handsome mutants in addition to serving as stock for further development in America. Some of the German hybrids of the *P. domesticum* group in cultivation include 'Die Braut' (The Bride), 'Graf Zeppelin,' and 'Schöne Illa' by Burger; 'Fürst Bismarck,' 'Feldmarschall Mackensen,' 'Frühlingszauber' ('Spring Magic' in translation), 'Onkel Richter' and 'Andenken an Carl Faiss' (syns. 'Neuheit C. Faiss,' 'Faiss Neuheit') by Faiss; 'Gartendirektor Siebert' and 'Gruss an Quedlinburg' (syn. Pride of Quedlinburg) by Bornemann.

Popular French forms include 'Mme. Thibaut' by Malet, 1867; 'Volante National Alba,' 1870's; and the dwarf 'Mme. Layal,' 1890's.

PELARGONIUM DOMESTICUM TODAY

P. × *domesticum* L. H. Bailey—Plants within this group are erect, woody stemmed, shrubby and densely leafy; they grow from one to three feet tall or more depending upon the variety. On the Pacific Coast *P. domesticum* is extensively used outdoors, especially for bedding. In climates unsuited for outdoor culture the year around, these plants are popular as ornamental pot-plants for the terrace, patio, porch, sunroom or window garden. The handsome, large flowers are frequently used for corsages or other decorative purposes.

The leaves of *P. domesticum* vary in shape from rigid heart-shaped with shallow angular lobes to softer-textured, lobeless, heart-shaped forms; both kinds are usually prominently veined. Excepting on dwarf types, they average about three inches across.

Dwarfs such as 'Mme. Layal' grow as tall (about a foot) as other low-growing forms within the group, but the leaves are considerably smaller in that they rarely exceed an inch in size, and the flowers are almost as large as the leaves. The color pattern of a flower suggests that of a pansy, and because of this fancied resemblance, these plants and certain of the larger forms are commonly referred to as "Pansy" pelargoniums.

P. domesticum cultivars are distinguished for their large, colorful, and often heavily ornamented flowers. The clusters are usually branched and are frequently very large. Individual flowers of the largest may attain a size of over three inches and are usually five-petaled; there are a few exceptions in that some kinds produce flowers with six or seven petals. There is one double-flowered form in cultivation—'La Primera.' Flowers may be flat or the petal margins may undulate; those of other plants may be ruffled and curled to such an extent that the flowers appear to be double in form.

Monotoned flowers within the group are rare; flowers of two colors are not usual; three to five colors or shades are general. Colors frequently blend or overlay one another whether shades of one color or two or more unrelated ones. In heavily "painted" flowers, colors appear to be superimposed one upon the other in the form of wash-painting, blotches, splashes, lines, veining, feathering or large "eyes" slightly darker than the base color, or darker colors through maroon, brown-black, very dark purple to black. "Eyes" and blotches are usually velvet-like and the surrounding areas suggest taffeta or the glossier texture of satin.

White and orchid to purple-flowered forms of *P. domesticum* simulate the coloring of certain classes of orchids. In addition to these colors there is a wide range from pastel hues through vivid shades of pink, salmon, and red to dark shades approaching black. It is necessary to point out that light tones sometimes vary slightly because of the environment in which the plants are grown; usually the colors are more vivid if abundant sunlight is available.

In attempting an arrangement under flower color heading, arbitrary choices were necessary in a few cases in order to point up a color tint no matter how slight, or for comparative reasons so as to distinguish one plant from another more easily. A few dwarf forms are listed on page 100, the remainder are listed as follows: white and tinted white, page 80; orchid, lavender and purple in light shades, page 82; and in dark shades, page 85; pastel pinks, page 86; pink, rose pink and rose, page 88; salmon and salmon tinted, page 91; red shades, page 94; and lastly very deep reds and purple, page 98.

SELECTED CULTIVARS OF P. DOMESTICUM

(Pelargoniums of Gardeners)

White and White Tinted

'Anita' (syn. 'Neptune')—Flowers white, light pink margins, dark eye in upper petals. England, 1890's.

'Alameda'—Flowers large, lilac white, violet blotch on upper petals, lower petals feathered violet. California.

'Baby' (syn. 'Baby Jarrett')—Flowers small, white, flushed pink, small red dot on each petal. Developed by Mrs. Clara Sue Jarrett.

'Cecelia Kellogg'—Flowers pink with white center and margins, margins ruffled. Jarrett.

'Chalee'—Flowers white with small orchid pink marks in center of all petals. Brown, California.

'Champion'—Flowers white, flushed pale pink, maroon spot on upper petals, small carmine spot on lower petals. England, 1897.

'City of Oakland'—Low growing; flowers large, white, upper petals veined to medium-large blotch of rosy violet; flower clusters large.

'Clara Angenette'—Flowers white with long orchid lavender blotch, margins ruffled. Distributed by Rober, 1940.

'Crusader'—Flowers white, faintly flushed pink, deep crimson blotch on upper petals, lower petals penciled crimson. Schmidt, 1947.

'Die Braut' (translation, 'The Bride')—Plant small; flowers white in center, shading to soft pink. Burger, Germany. Introduced into America, 1900.

'Duchess of Edinburgh'—Flowers large, white, ruffled, upper petals marked with deep purple blotch. England, 1895.

'Edith Cavell'—Flowers large, white, a maroon blotch on all petals, each blotch surrounded by rose pink. Introduced about 1920.

'Estralita'—Flowers white with black blotch surrounded by red on upper petals. Rober.

'Gay Nineties'—Flowers large, white, the upper petals heavily veined from a large raspberry-rose blotch, a few deep rose stripes on lower petals. Schmidt, 1947.

'Grace Armstrong'—Flowers large, white, a small mallow-purple spot on upper petals.

'Grandma Zim'—Flowers white shading to blush pink, purple blotch in upper petals. Rober, 1940's.

'Jarretts Moonbeam'—Flowers white with violet veins on lower petals, velvety black blotch outlined by crimson on upper petals. Jarrett, California.

'Leonore'—Flowers white, upper petals maroon blotched, lower petals slightly marked, margins ruffled. Rober.

'Lord Clyde'—Flowers white, veined and tinged light violet, velvety crimson blotch on all petals. Introduced from England, 1913.

'Maid of Kent' (syn. 'Duchess of Kent')—Tall; flowers large, white, a small pale purple mark on upper petals, margins ruffled. England, 1880.

'Mardi Gras'—Flowers white, upper petals marked and blotched violet rose. Schmidt.

'Mary Bard'—Flowers white, slight mallow-purple marking at base of petals.

'Miss Saunders' (syns. 'Mrs. Saunders,' 'Mrs. Sanders'; erroneous names, 'Frau Krumb,' 'Frau Krump')—Flowers large, white, the upper petals broadly blotched with purple crimson. Introduced from England, 1913.

'Montecito'—Flowers white flushed orchid pink, a dark blotch on all petals. California.

'Neale Warren'—Flowers large, white, a purple blotch on all petals. California.

'Nitida'—Flowers large, white, the upper petals faintly pink flushed, and marked with a dark violet blotch.

'Olympe' (syn. 'Olympic')—Flowers large, white, a small orchid blotch and veins on upper petals. Introduced by Howard & Smith, 1913.

'Onkel Richter'—Small; flowers white with dark purple blotch on upper petals. Faiss, Germany. Introduced into America about 1910.

'Pearly Queen'—Flowers large, white, faintly flushed pink, a velvety dark red spot on upper petals. the margins ruffled. Brown.

'Shasta'—Flowers white with faint marks in throat.

'Saint Francis'—Tall growing; flowers white with lilac undertone, a large velvety black-red spot in upper petals, smaller red spot and crimson veins in lower petals.

'Sunburst'—Flowers medium large, white with faint lilac undertone, a large raspberry-red blotch and splashes in upper petals, the margins ruffled. Brown.

'Volante National Alba'—Flowers large, white with slight lavender marks at base of petals. Originated in France, 1870's.

Orchid, Lavender, and Purple Flowers

'Alabama'—Flowers large, deep orchid, with a violet-black spot on upper petals, lower petals paler with smaller violet spot.

'Andenken an Carl Faiss' (syns. 'Neuheit C. Faiss,' 'Faiss Neuheit') —Flowers silvery bluish orchid with elongated velvety violet-black blotch on all petals, veined deep violet at base of petals. Named in Germany for the developer, who originally distributed it as a "novelty" (Neuheit). Distinctive.

'Andenken an Moskow'—Flowers dark lavender with black eyes on all petals.

'Anna Stager'—Flowers large, mallow pink shading to white, a dark blotch in upper petals. Rober.

'Beautiful'—Mutant of 'Oster Gruss.' Flowers lavender pink with dark blotch in all petals.

'Bel Air'—Flowers delicate orchid pink to lilac, a dark blotch in upper petals. Rober.

'Beverly Hills'—Flowers violet-pink, crimson veined from base to small deep violet blotch on upper petals.

Plate 1   The long-familiar garden geranium, *Pelargonium hortorum*, in an outdoor planting. This is also the most common type for indoor use. *Gottscho-Schleisner* photo.

Plate 2 Four distinctive cultivars, or varieties, of *Pelargonium hortorum*. *Upper left:* 'Distinction'; *upper right:* 'Shirley Summers'; *lower left:* 'Fiat Queen'; *lower right:* 'Carrousel.' *Courtesy of Milton H. Arndt.*

Plate 3 A group of colored-leaved geraniums. *Upper row,* left to right: 'Wilhelm Langgluth,' 'Jubilee,' 'Happy Thought'; *middle row:* 'Carlton Velma,' 'Maximilian,' 'French Lace'; *lower row:* 'Skies of Italy,' 'Miss Burdett Coutts,' 'Crystal Palace Gem.' *Courtesy of Milton H. Arndt.*

Plate 4 *Pelargonium domesticum* plants of three sorts. *Upper left:* 'Torento.' *Upper right:* a Danish clone, showing the influence of *P. cucullatum* in the leaves. *Courtesy of J. E. Ohlsens Enke, Copenhagen. Below:* 'Clorinda.' *This and 'To-rento' by courtesy of Logee's Greenhouses.*

Plate 5   More *P. domesticum* varieties. *Above:* Empress of Russia. *Courtesy of Paul J. Howard. Below:* 'Merle,' showing the influence of *P. angulosum* in the leaves. *Courtesy of Catherine McCollum.*

Plate 6   *Above: Pelargonium angulosum,* a branch picked from the mountain slope on opposite page. *Below:* 'White Lady.' *Courtesy of Milton H. Arndt.*

Plate 7 *Pelargonium angulosum* growing wild in the mountains near Cape-town, South Africa. *Courtesy of Mildred Capron.*

Plate 8 Above: *P. odoratissimum,* one of the scented-leaved species in full flower. *Courtesy of Logee's Greenhouses.* Below: *P. crithmifolium,* a South African species with fleshy stems of woody texture, fibrous roots, and deciduous leaves. *Courtesy of New York Botanical Garden.*

Plate 9 Scented-leaved geraniums. *Upper left: Pelargonium citrosum* (formerly called *P. citriodorum*); *upper left: P. crispum; lower left: P. melissinum; lower right: P. denticulatum. J. Horace McFarland photos.*

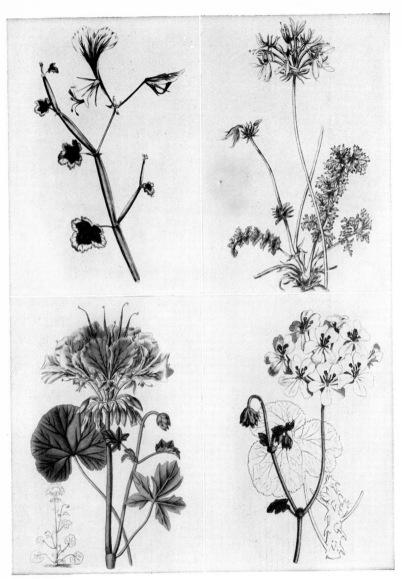

Plate 10 Rare and unusual species of *Pelargonium. Upper left:* P. *tetragonum; upper right:* P. *rapaceum; lower left:* P. *endlicherianum; lower right:* P. *echinatum. Pictures from early books, by courtesy of the American Philosophical Society.*

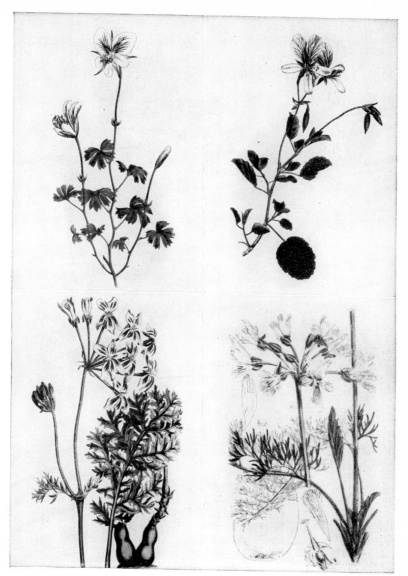

Plate 11 *Upper left: P. praemorsum* (formerly called *P. quinatum*); *upper right: P. betulinum; lower left: P. triste; lower right: P. bowkeri. Courtesy of the American Philosophical Society.*

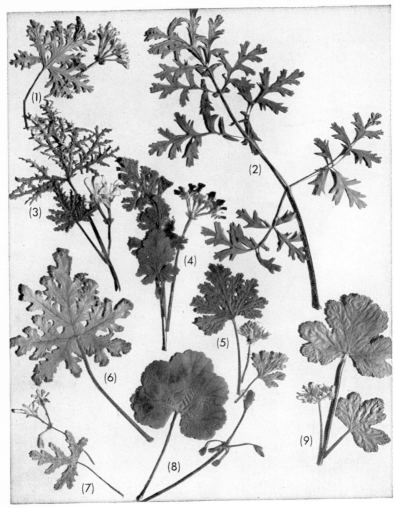

Plate 12   Leaf and flower specimens from living plants. 1: *P. blandfordianum*;
2: *P. apiifolium*; 3: *P. denticulatum* 'Filicifolium'; 4: 'Concolor Lace'; 5: 'Little
Gem'; 6: 'Topsy'; 7: 'Mopsy'; 8: *P. frutetorum*; 9: A scented-leaved hybrid often
called *P. melissinum* (see also *P. melissinum* on Plate 9).

Plate 13 Specimens from living plants. 1: *P. pinnatum*; 2: *P. bowkeri*; 3: *P. carnosum*; 4: *P. paradoxum*; 5: *P. acetosum*; 6: 'Fingered Flowers'; 7: *P. radens*, young leaf; 8: *P. radens*, more developed leaf.

Plate 14   Specimens from living plants. 1: P. *glaucifolium*; 2: P. *fulgidum*; 3: P. *dasycaule*; 4: 'Scarlet Unique'; 5: 'Capri'; 6: P. *cordifolium* (formerly called P. *cordatum*); 7: P. *ardens*; 8: 'Rollisons Unique'; 9: 'Mrs. Kingsley'; 10: P. *echinatum*; 11: P. *scarboroviae*; 12: P. *hispidum*; 13: P. *bicolor*; 14: P. *cotyledonis*; 15: P. *gibbosum*; 16: P. *crassicaule*.

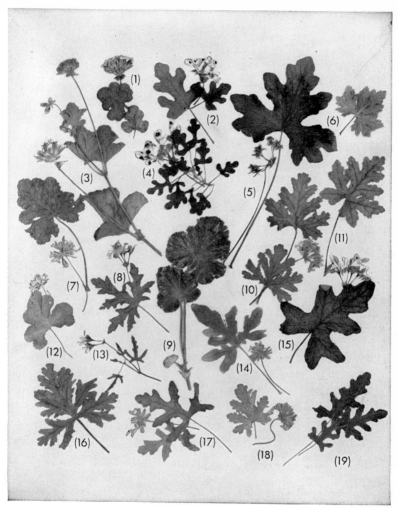

Plate 15 Specimens from living plants. 1: 'Fringed Oak'; 2: *P. quercifolium*; 3: 'Skeltons Unique'; 4: 'Fair Ellen'; 5; 'Beauty Oak'; 6: 'Pretty Polly'; 7: 'Attar of Roses'; 8: *P. viscosissimum*; 9: 'Logees Snowflake'; 10: 'Camphor Rose'; 11: 'Mrs. Taylor'; 12: *P. capitatum*; 13: *P. jatrophaefolium*; 14: 'Robers Lemon Rose'; 15: 'Haviland'; 16: *P. scabrum* 'M. Ninon'; 17: 'Village Hill Oak'; 18; 'Elkhorn'; 19: 'Staghorn.'

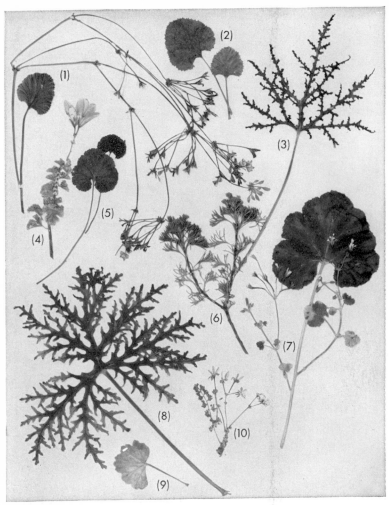

Plate 16 Specimen from living plants. 1: *P. reniforme*; 2: *P. nervosum*; 3: 'Carlton Fern'; 4: 'Variegated Prince Rupert'; 5: *P. grossularioides*; 6: *P. abrotanifolium*; 7: **P. odoratissimum**; 8: 'Carlton Corsage'; 9: *P. burtoniae*; 10: *P. alternans.*

'Caprice'—Flowers pale lavender with dark marking on all petals. Rober, 1946.

'Chino' (syn. 'Antoinette')—Upper petals purple surrounded by violet-rose and edged with white, lower petals white with orchid tinge.

'Cho Cho San'—Flowers lavender, dark spot on upper petals, small red spot on lower petals.

'Christie'—Flowers large, orchid pink, a raspberry-red blotch on upper petals, all petals veined raspberry-red.

'Clara Huntington'—Flower clusters large; flowers light cyclamen purple with large dark purple blotch on upper petals. Rober.

'Dainty Lady'—Flowers large, lilac pink, a red blotch on upper petals, lower petals paler with smaller rosy red spot.

'De Vega'—Flowers lilac lavender with dark blotch on upper petals.

'Deutscher Ruhm' (translation, 'German Glory')—Flower clusters large, flowers light violet-pink, dark eyes in upper petals. Introduced from Germany, 1906.

'Dieners Thirty-Six'—Similar to 'Thirty-Three' (below) but not as deeply colored. Diener.

'Dieners Thirty-Three'—Flowers large, orchid lavender, violet-purple blotch in upper petals, all petals feathered, margins ruffled. Distinctive. Diener.

'Discovery'—Tall, vigorous; flower clusters large; flowers large, light orchid-pink, upper petals heavily blotched, all petal margins waved. California, 1951.

'Edith Pruner'—Flowers small, orchid-pink at throat deepening to violet—a symphony of violet shades.

'Fürst Bismarck' (syn. 'Prince Bismarck')—Similar to the preceding except that the flowers are lighter in color, blotch on petals is red-black. Faiss, 1898.

'Gladys Leslie'—Flowers pale rosy violet, dark blotch on upper petals.

'Iris'—Upper petals light lilac-lavender, heavily veined and marked light and deep violet, lower petals pale lilac shading to almost white at throat; the large flower is elongated in shape. Distinctive. Brown.

'John Martin'—Flowers orchid-pink with cherry-red blotches, white at throat.

'Lavender Quedlinburg'—Flowers lavender with purple blotch on upper petals, lower petals white at base. Mutant of 'Gruss an Quedlinburg.'

'Lavender Queen'—Flower clusters large; flowers lavender with darker spot on all petals.

'Lady Gay'—Flowers deep phlox pink, pale purple throat, dark blotch on upper petals.

'Lilac Time'—Flowers medium large, lilac; small dark violet blotch on upper petals, flushed and veined rosy violet; no marking on lower petals. California, 1947.

'Louise Dixon'—Flowers light mauve pink with purple blotch on all petals.

'Lucille Kluthes'—Flowers light amaranth pink with light red marking.

'Lucretia Smith'—Tall habit of growth; flowers large, orchid pink, deep crimson blotch on all petals. Rober.

'Majesta'—Tall growing; flowers large, mauve lavender, dark blotch on upper petals.

'Matilda Rassau'—Flowers large, lavender pink with purple blotch on upper petals.

'May Queen'—Flowers orchid with red blotch on upper petals. California, 1938.

'Merle'—Flowers light orchid with medium-sized purple blotch on upper petals. California.

'Misty Rose'—Flowers pale magenta with dark blotch on upper petals. Rober.

'Orchid Edith North'—Mutant of 'Edith North.' Flowers orchid pink with darker blotch on upper petals.

'Orchid Sue Jarrett'—Flowers large, lavender, with dark blotch on all petals.

'Palo Alto'—Flowers large, pale pinkish lavender, a dark violet blotch on upper petals. Jarrett.

'Princess'—Flowers lavender with slight marking.

'Purple Señorita'—Upper petals lilac shading to rose magenta at base, feathered deep magenta, the lower petals rosy-pink at base paling toward margins. Rober.

'Rebecca Parker'—Flowers medium, lavender, with large maroon blotch on upper petals, rosy lilac flushed; lower petals with small violet flecks. California, 1947.

'San Diego'—Flowers soft rosy lilac with velvety maroon blotches, the margins ruffled.

'San Marino'—Flowers deep orchid lavender with maroon blotches. California.

'Stardust'—Flower clusters large; flowers large, frosty pale lavender, veined rosy violet; deep violet spot and flush of rose on upper petals. Kerrigan, 1942.

'Silver Lining'—Flowers medium large, lavender, rose flushed, a large black blotch on all petals, margins pale silvery lavender. California, 1947.

'Troubadour'—Flowers large, upper petals maroon black with rosy violet margins shading to lilac at the edge; lower petals pale lilac, veined and tinted rosy violet. Kerrigan, 1942.

'Walter Oertel'—Upper petals mulberry with lighter edge; lower petals orchid pink with mulberry blotch. Evans, 1947.

'Waltztime'—Mutant of 'Ruth Eleanor.' Flower clusters large; flowers large, orchid lavender, with violet blotch and veining on upper petals. Schmidt. 1942.

Darker Orchid and Purple Shades

'Bermuda'—Flowers fuchsia-purple with dark blotches. Rober.

'Blue Mabel' (syn. 'Smoky Purple')—Color pattern similar to that of 'Mabel' (below), except that upper petals are edged with lavender, and the outer half of each lower petal is lavender.

'Charlotte Brice' (syn. 'Blue Boy')—Flowers fuchsia purple, paling toward the margins, upper petals very slightly marked. Rober.

'Conchita'—Flowers deep velvety purple paling toward the throat.

'Dark Mabel' (syn. 'Dark Presidio')—Similar in pattern to 'Blue Mabel' except that the dark area in the upper petals is dark grape purple and the margins are pink; lower petals are lavender and white.

'Dusky Belle'—Flowers medium large, upper petals velvety brownish black with narrow rosy lilac margins; lower petals lilac, peculiarly veined and flushed rosy violet on outer half of petals. California.

'Elizabeth Bodger'—Flowers light violet with large dark blotch on upper petals, smaller blotch on lower petals. Rober.

'Ethel Stanley'—Flowers of blended violet shade, petunia-purple in center, paling toward the margins.

'Haile Selassie'—Flowers pinkish lavender, paling slightly toward the margins, velvety brown blotch on all petals.

'Mabel'—Flowers large, upper petals maroon with narrow pink edge; lower petals rose pink halfway to white at base. Distinctive. England, 1879.

'Marie Rober'—Flowers lavender violet with large, black, velvety blotch on all petals. Good habit and color. Rober.

Pastel Pink Tones

'Ballerina'—Medium tall; flowers large, shell pink, with crimson spot on upper petals, the margins ruffled. Schmidt.

'Bessie Marsh'—Flowers pale pink, the petals red blotched and veined.

'Bettina'—Flowers large, pink, the upper petals prominently veined from the base to a medium large, deep velvety red blotch; lower petals paler pink, dark veined toward base. Introduced by Schmidt, 1949.

'Cover Girl'—Flowers soft pink, upper petals deeper pink with white throat. California, 1951.

'Debutante'—Flowers large, silvery rose pink, with velvety brown-black blotch and crimson veins on upper petals. Schmidt.

'Dorothy'—Flowers blush pink with red spots. England, 1890's.

'Fascination'—Flowers soft pink with dark blotch on upper petals. England.

'Frühlingszauber' (translation, 'Spring Magic')—Habit low, compact; flowers large, white, tinged pink, with red blotch on upper petals, the margins waved. Faiss.

'Gartendirektor Siebert'—Flowers small, shell pink with dark eyes on all petals. Bornemann, 1890's.

'Harmony'—Flowers of blended rose pink, with dark spot on upper petals; red spot on lower petals; throat white.

'Jarretts Beauty'—Flowers fuchsine-pink, a long dark blotch on all petals. Jarrett, 1930's.

'Kathe Bornemann'—Flowers small, the lower petals white with pink tinge; upper petals pink with salmon tint, veined and blotched crimson, the margins waved. Germany, introduced in 1906.

'La Primera'—Tall; leaves light green; flower clusters large; flowers medium large, cupped, double with twenty or more petals in each; soft light pink, white streaked, the margins edged white; outer petals waved, inner petals curled or twisted. Introduced from Mexico by Arndt, 1949.

'Leading Lady'—Lower petals pink paling to white in throat; upper petals bright pink with large velvety black blotch streaking toward the margins. Kerrigan, 1942.

'Maud Hooper'—Flowers small, pale pink deepening toward the center, upper petals feathered rose. England, 1890's.

'Madame Thibaut'—Flowers Dresden pink painted over white, the white showing irregularly at throat and margins, a crimson-maroon blotch on upper petals, the margins heavily ruffled. Arthur Malet, France, 1867.

'Mrs. Harrison' (syn. 'Lady Harrison')—Flowers large, petals white, washed rose pink, the upper petals crimson veined, lower petals rose veined, margins ruffled. England, 1873.

'Mrs. Hugh Evans'—Flowers rose pink, white at throat, all petals bright veined. Rober.

'Our Francis'—Habit of growth low, compact; flowers silvery rose pink, the upper petals deeper pink with crimson blotch, margins waved.

'Pauline Schroeter'—Flowers Dresden pink with white blotch on lower petals; upper petals deeper pink with dark blotch. Introduced from Germany, 1913.

'Peggy Craddock'—Compact and low growing; flowers light silvery pink, few crimson veins from base of petals to strawberry-pink blotch.

'Ray Kellogg'—Flowers large, pale pink, flushed strawberry pink, the upper petals heavily veined from base to a velvety black blotch; lower petals with small round maroon spot and slight orchid-pink veining in lighter throat. Jarrett.

'Ruth Eleanor'—Tall; flowers large, soft rose pink, the margins ruffled. California, 1938.

'Santa Monica'—Flowers La France pink with deep red spots on upper petals surrounded by rose pink.

'Schöne Illa'—Flower clusters large; flowers medium large, the lower petals shell pink with orchid undertone and small red lines at base; upper petals veined and blotched deep crimson and rose red. Burger, Germany, 1898.

'Valentine Girl'—Flowers large, the upper petals shell pink with red-orange spot; lower petals pale pink.

'Vera N. Watt'—Tall growing; flowers rosy pink with crimson spot on upper petals, margins ruffled. California.

Pink, Rose Pink, and Rose

'Alice Eastwood'—Flower clusters large; flowers large, soft rose pink; upper petals brighter pink, veined from the base to a medium-large, deep red velvety spot, the margins waved. Schmidt, 1948.

'Americana'—Habit of growth medium large; flowers large, pink, all petals veined and blotched brown black; upper petals tinged with orange.

'Arborea'—Flowers small, rose magenta shading to rose pink in the center. An old hybrid of obscure origin.

'Bataan'—Flowers rose pink with narrow white margins, a red blotch on all petals. Rober. 1945.

'Bertha Wagner'—Flowers large, carmine pink, the margins edged white, a dark blotch on upper petals. Introduced from Germany, 1913.

'Betty Lee Schatz'—Flowers medium large, the upper petals pink and crimson, lower petals pink.

'Burlesque'—Flowers large, rose pink, white at throat and margins, the upper petals veined and slightly blotched deep violet, the margins waved and curled. Schmidt, 1942.

'Cassandra'—Flowers pink, penciled rose.

'Chicago Market'—Low growing; flowers large, rose pink, with rose red blotch in upper petals. Distributed before 1935.

'China Rose'—Flowers large, deep smoky cerise red, paling to almost white at the throat; upper petals heavily veined from base to large velvety brown-black blotch; small dark spot and deep red veining in lower petals. Introduced by Schmidt, 1949.

'Circus Day'—Flower clusters large; flowers very large; upper petals bright pink with medium-large velvety brown-black blotch, salmon flushed; lower petals lighter pink. Schmidt, 1951.

'Claire Evans'—Flowers deep rose pink with darker eyes on all petals. Evans, California.

'Dieners Giant' (syn. 'Pink Giant,' 'Venus')—Flowers large, clear soft pink with crimson blotch at base of upper petals. Diener.

'Duchess of Westminster'—Flowers medium large, the upper petals pink shaded with red, lower petals pale pink.

'Earl Watterson'—Flowers medium large, the upper petals rose pink, flushed orange around blackish blotch, lower petals soft rosy pink.

'Edith Rober'—Flowers La France pink with dark blotch in upper petals. Rober.

'Elsie Gilkey'—Flowers deep Dresden pink with white throat and dark maroon blotch on upper petals surrounded by scarlet. Jarrett.

'Elza Meyberg'—Flowers clear pink with dark blotch on upper petals, the margins ruffled. Rober, 1940.

'Ernie'—Flowers bright carmine pink with dark brown blotch on upper petals. the margins ruffled. Rober, 1946.

'Ernst Studerus'—Flowers solidly pink except for faint veining. Rober, 1940's.

'Felice Hammonds'—Flowers large, pink, paler at throat, crimson blotched. California.

'Fred Dorner'—Flowers white in center shading through carmine pink to white edge of margins, all petals crimson blotched. England, 1880's.

'Frau Krumb' (syn. 'Frau Krump')—Flowers soft rosy pink, upper petals blotched purplish red, the margins ruffled. Introduced from Germany, 1913.

'Garfield Park' (syn. 'Garfield Pink')—A mutant of 'Ostergruss'; flowers deep pink with blackish blotch on all petals.

'General Eisenhower'—Flowers bright rose pink with dark red blotch on upper petals.

'Geraldine'—Flowers bright pink with white throat and dark blotch on upper petals. Jarrett.

'Giant Venus' (syn. 'Venus')—Flowers large, light salmon pink, a dark maroon blotch streaking toward margins of upper petals, with small maroon blotch and feathering in lower petals. Diener.

'Glendale'—Similar to 'General Eisenhower' except that all petals are blotched. Rober.

'Goleta'—Flowers deep rose pink, a maroon blotch on upper petals surrounded by strawberry pink.

'Grandiosa'—Flowers light crimson shading to orange-tinted rose in the center.

'Gypsy Queen'—Flowers deep pink with white throat, blotched scarlet and black. Rober, late 1930's.

'Kate Sessions'—Flowers rose pink paling toward margins, dark blotched.

'Lessars Pride'—Flowers very large, pink; large black blotch in upper petals, scarlet flushed and veined; lower petals white toward throat. California, 1948.

'Lila'—Flower clusters large; flowers large, raspberry rose shading to pale pink at the margins, a large maroon blotch on all petals. Evans, 1947.

'Lois MacKay'—Flowers small, Tyrian pink, veined wine red.

'Lucy Ann Leslie' (syn. 'Lady Leslie')—Flowers large, ruffled, light rose pink, the upper petals crimson veined and blotched.

'Lucy Becker'—Mutant of 'Ostergruss'; the ground color of the flowers is pink but resembles the parent in all other respects.

'Mary Pickford'—Compact habit of growth; flowers rose pink with dark blotches. Rober.

'Masterpiece'—Flowers very large, strawberry pink; large brown-black blotch on all petals, dark veining from blotch toward the margins. California, 1947.

'Maxine Jarrett'—Flowers bright pink with dark violet blotch in upper petals. Jarrett.

'Melody'—Flowers rose pink, white throat, dark brown blotched.

'Montebella'—Flowers medium large, bright phlox pink with dark blotches, the margins waved.

'Mrs. Milton Sills'—Mutant of 'Lucy Becker'; flowers cerise pink with dark blotch on all petals.

'Mrs. O. W. Childs'—Low growing; flower clusters large; flowers rose pink, slightly brighter veined, the margins waved. England, 1890's.

'Mrs. Will Hays'—Flowers rose pink, the upper petals dark blotched and marked with white, lower petals paler pink, paling toward margins. Rober.

'Pink Charm'—Flowers medium large, the upper petals pink, flushed salmon, blotched brown, lower petals lighter pink.

'Pinky'—Flowers medium large, the upper petals pink veined and blotched red, lower petals lighter pink.

'Piru'—Flowers medium large, rose pink with dark red blotch surrounded by strawberry pink, the throat white. California.

'Prince Charming'—Flowers large, the upper petals pink, crimson blotched and veined, lower petals lighter pink with crimson veins.

'Princess Maud'—White throat and margins; large blotch of rosy carmine. A mutant of 'Volante Nationale' which it resembles except that the blotch is deeper in color. England, about 1900.

'Richard Diener' (syn. 'Diener's Giant,' 'Giant')—Flowers deep rich pink with streaked red blotch at base of upper petals. Named for the developer.

'Ripples'—Flowers light rose maroon with lilac undertone, all petals heavily veined, almost white at the margins. California, 1951.

'Robers Lullaby'—Flowers rose pink with white throat, a dark brown blotch on upper petals. Rober, early 1940's.

'Rosakoenigin' (translation, 'Pink Queen')—Habit of growth stocky, vigorous; flower clusters large; flowers large, rose red with white throat, a black velvety spot and veins in upper petals. Faiss. Introduced into America 1911.

'Rose Marie' (syn. 'Pink Vogel')—A pink-flowered mutant of 'Marie Vogel.'

'Rose Petals'—Flowers medium large, the upper petals violet rose, dark blotched, all petals white at base and margins.

'S. A. Breen'—Flowers large, the upper petals pink, veined purple, brown and orange blotched; lower petals shell pink.

'San Antonio'—Plants small, compact; showy rose flowers in large clusters. California.

'San Luis Rey'—Flowers very large, soft rose; maroon blotch in upper petals. California.

'San Mateo'—Flowers medium large, upper petals deep pink with crimson blotch, lower petals paler pink.

'Sport of Glendale'—Flowers phlox pink with maroon blotches. Rober, 1940.

'Spring Song'—Flowers large, the upper petals pink with velvety red blotch and crimson veins, lower petals lighter pink and crimson veined. Kerrigan, 1947.

'Springtime'—Flowers medium large, vivid pink, with white throat and irregular white margins, the edges waved rather than ruffled. The pink and white pattern varies.

'Sunlight' (syn. 'Rose Pink Jarrett')—Flowers bright pink with white streaks and blotches. Jarrett.

'Tiger Rose'—Habit compact; flowers rose pink with dark red streaks through all petals. Rober.

'Vida Burke'—Flowers large, the upper petals deep rose pink with velvety brown-black blotch surrounded by orange; lower petals lighter rose pink with darker mark through center. Cassidy.

Salmon and Salmon Tinted

'Adolph Topfer'—Flowers delicate salmon pink with dark blotch on upper petals. An old variety of obscure origin.

'Ardith'—Flowers bright salmon shading through cerise to lavender pink margins, with small maroon blotch and streaks on upper petals. Distributed by Hallowell, California.

'Brentwood'—Flowers salmon pink with maroon blotch on upper petals, the lower petals lighter salmon. Evans, 1946.

'California'—Flowers peach pink with crimson blotch and maroon streaks on upper petals. England, 1880's.

'Edith North'—Tall growing; flowers shaded soft salmon pink with brown blotch on upper petals, the lower petals lighter in color.

'Faiss Triumph'—Flowers very large, light rose pink (sometimes showing a slight salmon tint), white throat, red blotch on upper petals, the margins ruffled. Faiss.

'Flame'—Flowers medium large, salmon flushed with orange, paler at throat, the upper petals feathered crimson. Brown.

'Flaming Youth'—Flowers bright salmon rose with orange glow, the veins velvety black.

'Flora Belle Claus'—Flowers pink shading to salmon, veined and flushed rose red, a velvety brown blotch on upper petals. Introduced before 1940.

'Goldilocks'—Tall growing; flowers soft golden apricot flushed with orange. California, 1951.

'Graf Zeppelin'—Habit low growing; flowers large, salmon, with maroon blotch and orange flush on upper petals, a small blotch and two violet lines on lower petals. Burger, Germany.

'Grossmama Fischer (translation, 'Grandma Fischer')—Habit compact; flowers large, clear deep salmon, a brown-black blotch on all petals. Faiss.

'Gruss an Quedlinburg' (syn. 'Pride of Quedlinburg' *)—Habit of growth tall; flowers large, shading from pink to salmon pink, a dark blotch on upper petals, white at base of lower petals. Distinctive. Developed by Bornemann, Germany, 1890's.

'Irene Ritchie'—Flowers large, the upper petals orange salmon with narrow salmon pink margins, black blotched; lower petals light pink.

'Jane Evans'—Flowers deep salmon rose shading to almost white at center, a large maroon blotch on upper petals. Evans.

'Lachskoenigin' (translation, 'Salmon Queen')—Habit of growth

* Not a direct translation, since "Gruss" means "greeting."

tall; flowers medium large, soft light salmon pink with white throat, the margins waved and curled. Germany, 1925.

'Lois Edna Cox'—Flowers large, silvery salmon pink with small blotch on upper petals, the lower petals red veined.

'Maid Marian'—Flowers salmon pink with carmine blotches. California, 1939.

'Marktgaertners Freude' (syns. 'Gardeners Joy' (translation), 'Pink Gardeners Joy')—Flowers very large, pink with slight salmon tint, maroon blotch on upper petals surrounded by rose, a few colored veins in lower petals. Introduced from Germany 1912.

'Martha Dubois'—Flowers brilliant salmon, rose toward center, with dark blotch on upper petals. Rober.

'Mary Elizabeth'—Flowers soft salmon rose pink, lighter at throat, slightly veined at base of petals. England, 1876.

'Mary Monica'—Flowers rosy pink with salmon undertone, white throat, a dark blotch on upper petals surrounded by orange tint. Schmidt, 1946.

'Morgan Miles'—Flowers salmon pink, a maroon blotch on upper petals and dark scarlet spot on lower petals. California, 1930's.

'Mrs. Gary Cooper'—Flowers clear salmon with dark veins in all petals. Rober.

'Orange Tanager'—Flowers similar to those of 'Flame' (above), except for a small but definite spot on the upper petals and the orange tone less intense. Brown.

'Otokar Samohrd'—Small growing; flowers pink shading to salmon, the margins ruffled. Faiss, 1925.

'Peach Blow'—Flowers large, pale peach pink at margins, shading through light violet rose to a medium-large red blotch in center of petals, with deep crimson veining at base of petals. Cassidy. 1946.

'Prairie Fire'—Habit of growth medium tall; flowers large, upper petals brown black through orange salmon to pink margins; lower petals soft pink, flushed salmon orange and veined dark brown. Schmidt, 1948.

'Rhapsody'—Flowers large, the upper petals velvety crimson black, lower petals salmon pink tinged with orange. Kerrigan, 1942.

'Robers Ideal'—Flowers large, salmon rose, with white throat and dark blotch on upper petals. Rober, about 1945.

'Rose Zeppelin'—A mutant of 'Graf Zeppelin' which it resembles except that the base color is rose pink.

'**Ruth Ellen Kellogg**'—Flowers large, coral pink, a dark brown blotch on upper petals surrounded by orange scarlet; lower petals streaked orange scarlet from base. Jarrett, 1940.

'**Ruth W. McAfee**'—Flowers large, rosy salmon, a dark red blotch on upper petals, small red spot on lower petals. Introduced by R. M. Henley, Indiana, about 1942.

'**Salmon Chris**'—Habit of growth small; flowers large, salmon rose, lightly marked.

'**Salmon Splendor**'—Flowers large, salmon with apricot undertones, veined crimson, the margins waved. Flowers larger and pinker than 'Grossmama Fischer.' Kerrigan, 1942.

'**Santa Cruz**'—Mutant of 'Ruth W. McAfee.' Habit of growth compact; flowers large, light salmon pink. California, 1930's.

'**Señorita**'—Flowers vivid salmon red paling at throat, the upper petals velvety reddish brown, flushed orange, the margins of all petals light pink and ruffled. Introduced by Evans & Reeves.

'**Shangri La**'—Flowers larger and deeper in color than those of 'Lachskoenigin' (above).

'**Solano**'—Flowers coral pink feathered with dark maroon. Introduced by Paul J. Howard, California.

'**Sue Jarrett**'—Flowers large, salmon pink, with large maroon blotch on upper petals, small maroon spot on lower petals, veined and feathered to base, the margins waved. Distinctive. Jarrett.

'**Swabian Maid**'—Mutant of 'Ostergruss.' Flowers large, salmon, with black blotch at base of all petals. Distinctive.

'**Sunset Magazine**'—Mutant of 'Sue Jarrett' which it resembles except that the lower petals are lighter in color.

'**Sweetheart**'—Flowers small, rose pink with salmon overtones, red-brown blotch on upper petals.

'**Tangerine**'—Flowers large, deep salmon pink with orange glow, a dark maroon blotch on upper petals. Brown.

'**Verna**'—Flowers light satiny pink with salmon tint, a dark blotch on upper petals. California, about 1940.

Red Shades

'**Andenken an London**' (syns. 'Amanda,' 'Scarlet Beauty')—Flowers glowing scarlet with black blotch on upper petals, the throat white. Germany, 1890's.

'**Anna May Wong**'—Flowers Chinese red with small white throat. Rober, 1940.

'**Anna Rudloff**'—Flowers red with large dark eyes. An old variety of obscure origin.

'**Antique**'—Flowers large, Chinese rose red, with dark blotch on all petals. Rober, 1945.

'**Aristocrat**'—Flowers medium large, deep red with orange sheen, lilac at throat and margins of petals. Introduced in California, 1951.

'**Azalea**'—Flowers large, rose carmine, the lower petals lighter; color pattern same as that of 'Marie Vogel.'

'**Bella Donna**'—Flowers light crimson with small white throat, a dark blotch on upper petals. Rober.

'**Beverly Fabretti**'—Habit of growth low, bushy; flowers rose red, the margins waved. Introduced by Schmidt, about 1945.

'**Bonnie**'—Flowers scarlet, the throat white flushed lilac, black blotched.

'**Carmine King**'—Flowers large, cerise red, with long dark blotch on upper petals, dark veins from blotch to margins.

'**Cherry Ann**'—Flowers cerise red with maroon blotch on upper petals, lower petals cerise lavender. California, 1930's.

'**Copper Red Eye**'—Flowers coppery red with dark eye on all petals. California, 1930's.

'**Cyril Warren**'—Flowers bright rose red with orange overtones, maroon-black blotch and dark veins in upper petals. Warren's Nursery.

'**Dark Springtime**'—Flowers rose red with violet glow, white at throat and margins.

'**Eastern Star**'—Small growing; flowers light red with dark blotches. California, 1930's.

'**Elvira Varley**'—Flowers large, the upper petals crimson-black with pink margins, lower petals cerise pink with crimson spot.

'**Ernest Brunton**'—Flowers camellia red with large dark crimson blotch on petals. Rober, 1945.

'**Ethelyn**'—Flowers red with crimson glow, white at base of upper petals, lilac at base of lower petals. California, 1930's.

'**Fandango**'—Flowers similar to those of 'Anna Rudloff' (above) except that the red is more intense.

'**Feldmarschall Mackensen**' (syn. 'Mackensen')—Flower clusters large; flowers large, fiery rose red without markings, crimson at base of upper petals; sometimes seven-petaled. Faiss.

'Fiesta Lady'—Flowers bright cerise rose with lilac undertones and orange flush; white throat and margins, the margins ruffled.

'Firefly'—Tall growing; flowers very small, fiery scarlet, with white throat. An old hybrid of English origin, 1850–1860.

'General MacArthur'—Flowers deep rose red with dark red blotch in upper petals. California, 1944.

'Gladys Kellogg'—Flowers glowing red with pale pink throat, a dark brown blotch on all petals. Jarrett.

'Grand Slam'—Habit of growth medium large; leaves medium large; flowers large, heavily waved; upper petals veined deep violet red from base to medium-large, velvety, red-brown spot, rosy red and salmon flushed at margins; lower petals rosy red with slight salmon undertone, the base of petals lightly marked and with a few purple veins. Developed by Schmidt, 1950.

'Gypsy'—Flowers dark cherry red, lighter at the margins. California, 1930's.

'Harriette'—Flowers medium large, crimson, veined maroon black to the dark velvety center, the narrow margins rose lilac. Cassidy.

'Heartbeat'—Flowers rose red with white throat and margins. One of Kerrigan's 'Springtime' series.

'Ida Henley'—Mutant of 'Ostergruss.' All petals velvety maroon with rose-red margins. Introduced 1938.

'John Wintermute'—Flowers large, raspberry rose overlaid with maroon and dark veining, somewhat lighter at throat and margins. Originated about 1942.

'Joan Fontaine'—Flowers very large, velvety black maroon, red at margins, violet throat. Distinctive.

'Joyce'—Upper petals cerise red overlaid with crimson and maroon, black veined toward margins; lower petals lighter and shading through mallow purple to white at base.

'Karminkoenigin' (translation, 'Carmine Queen')—Small habit of growth; flowers carmine red with dark blotch on upper petals. Faiss, 1925.

'Louise Sanborn'—Flowers bright scarlet with white throat, a dark blotch and red veining on all petals. Somewhat similar to 'Andenken an London' but the flowers are larger and the margins more ruffled and more white at throat.

'Lowell'—Flowers terracotta red with black blotch on all petals. England, 1890's.

'Marie Vogel'—Flowers large, the upper petals scarlet with small black blotch and feathering; lower petals crimson without marking, the margins ruffled. Distinctive. Developed by Faiss, introduced into America, 1925.

'Milada C'erny'—Flowers red with white throat, orchid pink at margins, a dark red velvety blotch on all petals. Rober, 1938.

'Mildred Orpet'—Flowers large, cherry red with dark markings on upper petals, smaller dark markings on lower petals. Rober, 1945.

'Milton'—Dark maroon blotch in upper petals surrounded by crimson and edged rose red at margins; lower petals soft pink shading to white at the base, crimson feathered. England, 1880's.

'Mont Pelée'—Flowers small, carmine shading to white center. California, about 1938.

'Mother Zim'—Flowers crimson shading to carmine at the margins, a dark blotch on upper petals, slight marking on lower petals. Rober, 1930's.

'Mrs. F. Bachler'—Flowers large, luminous deep salmon rose red with dark blotches. Diener, 1930's.

'Ostergruss'—(translation, 'Easter Greeting')—Flowers medium large, bright red with vermilion overtones, a large black blotch on all petals. One of the earliest flowering varieties. Introduced from Germany, 1906.

'Pasadena'—Flowers rose-red with maroon blotch on upper petals. Diener, California, 1940.

'Paso Robles'—Flowers large, carmine, with a large dark red spot on upper petals and small dark crimson spot on lower petals. California, about 1942.

'Patty Hurst'—Flowers medium large, the upper petals orange-scarlet with black blotch, lower petals scarlet shading lighter toward the base.

'Peter Hoser'—Flowers large, brilliant brick red, a black blotch on upper petals, small crimson spot on lower petals. Germany, 1906.

'Professor Correns'—Flowers bright cherry red with black spots on lower petals. California, 1930's.

'Queen of Hearts'—Flowers medium large, deep rose red, the upper petals orange flushed around black blotch. Bohanan, 1946.

'Red Cross'—Flowers large, rose red, orange flushed, maroon blotched.

'Red Moon'—Flowers large, light rose red with orange overtone, upper petals darker toned with velvety dark brown blotch. Cassidy.

'Rita Long'—Flowers large, the upper petals satiny black bordered with red at margins, lower petals rose red. Cassidy.

'Sensation'—Flowers large, crimson, with dark red blotch on all petals, the margins ruffled. An old variety of obscure origin.

'Westwood'—Flowers large, the upper petals scarlet with velvety black blotch, orchid pink at margins; lower petals orchid pink, flushed rose pink and veined to throat from small dark blotch. Rober, 1930.

'Wolfgang von Goethe'—Flowers large, dark red with violet-black eye in all petals. Introduced from Germany, 1906.

'Wurtembergia'—Mutant of 'Ostergruss.' Flowers large, dark red, with large violet-black blotch on all petals. California.

'Zinfandel'—Habit of growth small; flowers glowing red with dark blotches. Origin obscure.

'Zinnobia' (syn. 'Zanobia')—Flowers medium large, the upper petals velvety crimson, shading lighter toward the margins; lower petals lighter crimson shading to vermilion toward margins, the edges waved and curled. Distinctive color. Introduced from Germany. 1910.

Dark Colors

'Anastasia'—Flowers soft mahogany red with darker blotches.

'Arabia'—Flowers maroon red with irregular white margins.

'Burgundy'—Flower buds dark Burgundy red opening to wine red overlaid with velvetlike reddish black, the margins ruffled. Brown, 1947.

'Belle of Africa'—A meritorious addition to the swarthy flowered group. Habit of growth large; flowers large, to three inches or more, slightly longer than broad, all petals very dark red overlaid with black velvet bloom, and penciled pink around the edges; center of flower pink with red veins; flower buds black with hairline edge of pink. Arndt, 1954.

'Congo'—Flowers medium large, maroon black at center surrounded by violet rose, paling to lilac at margins. Kerrigan, 1947.

'Conspicuous'—Flowers very large, wine red with black blotch and veining on upper petals, elongated black spot on lower petals, the margins of petals edged with hairline of black, waved. Brown, 1947.

'Don Juan'—Flowers medium large, dark red, all petals veined and blotched brown black. Kerrigan, 1942.

'Duchess of Cornwall'—Flowers large, maroon with narrow pink margins on upper petals, the lower petals maroon with wider pink margins. Introduced by Germain, 1948. Not related to 'Empress of Russia' (syn. 'Black Pansy'; erroneous name, 'Emperor of Russia') Flowers very dark in the center shading through purplish maroon to narrow white or near white at edge of petals. England, 1882.

'Empress of Russia'—Flowers lavender white in center, with large dark maroon blotch on all petals surrounded by crimson purple, and narrowly edged with white. England, 1882.

'Gypsy Love'—Flowers maroon edged with white.

'Helen Beebe'—Flowers medium large, the upper petals maroon with rose margins; lower petals white, flushed pink, marked with purple.

'Irene Ditmer'—Flowers velvety black, tinted and veined with raspberry red to the white margins.

'James Weldon'—Flowers bronze brown, light crimson toward margins of upper petals; lower petals strawberry pink with small bronzy blotch. Rober, about 1940.

'Jessie Jarrett'—Flowers dark violet rose with maroon blotch on all petals. Jarrett.

'Joann'—Flowers of blended and striped maroon.

'Jungle Night'—Flowers maroon overlaid with velvety black, Burgundy red toward edge, the margins ruffled and curled. Brown, 1941.

'Mandalay'—Flowers very large and ruffled, a very large velvety black blotch on all petals, flushed rose, with lavender at edge of margins. California, 1947.

'Mary B. Quinlan'—Flowers dark wine red at throat and margins, overlaid with velvety black in center of petals, the margins waved. Brown, 1941.

'Nell Bertram'—Flowers medium large, a brown-black blotch on all petals surrounded by bright pink, shading to pale lilac pink at the margins, the base of petals heavily black veined. Introduced by Schmidt, 1947.

'Oriental'—Black velvetlike blotch on all petals surrounded by strawberry pink, crimson veined, the margins pink.

'Purple Beauty'—Habit of growth medium tall; flower clusters large; flowers large, solidly very dark purple except for the very narrow pink edges of all petals. Developed by Arndt, 1949.

'Red Velvet'—Flowers slightly darker than 'Burgundy,' black veined from large velvety black blotch to base of petals. Brown, 1941.

'Royal Robe'—Flowers large, bright mahogany red, orchid pink at edge of margins.

'Ruffled Oriental'—Flowers mulberry red, all petals overlaid with black blotch, the margins of petals narrowly edged light lavender, the edges ruffled.

'Thundercloud'—Flowers medium large, dark purple, with black blotch and veins on all petals, the margins lavender, ruffled. California, 1947.

'Vagabond'—Mutant of 'Joyce.' Flowers large, deep velvety maroon with white center. Schmidt, 1947.

'Zulu King'—Medium-large habit of growth; flowers large; upper petals almost entirely velvety brown black; lower petals rosy red, lilac at margins, with black blotch and veins. California, 1951.

Dwarf Forms of Pelargonium Domesticum

'Baby Breen'—Dwarf habit of growth; flowers larger than those of 'Little Rascal' (below), blended lilac and deep velvety purple. Introduced by Schmidt, 1949.

'Baby Snooks'—Habit of growth small; flowers lavender; lower petals very pale orchid pink, upper petals of same base color with heavy rose-violet veins and deep red black blotch in center, flushed raspberry toward petal margins. Introduced by Henley, 1953.

'Chickadee'—Habit small; flowers lavender; a deep violet blotch in upper petals, smaller blotch in lower petals. Introduced by Henley, 1953.

'Earliana'—Habit of growth similar to 'Mme. Layal'; the color pattern of the flowers is similar, but maroon takes the place of purple. Originated in California before 1935.

'Little Rascal'—Similar to 'Mme. Layal' in habit of growth; upper petals of flowers veined from base to velvety maroon black blotch, tinted rosy violet toward lilac margins; lower petals lilac white. Schmidt, 1947.

'Madame Layal' (commonly called the "Pansy pelargonium")—Habit of growth small, bushy; leaves small, to about an inch; flowers small, the upper petals dark violet purple shading through rose to the narrow white margins; lower petals white, tinted and veined light violet rose. France.

Chapter 4

SCENTED-LEAVED GERANIUMS

Geraniums with fragrant leaves have an intimate appeal not possessed by those whose claim for attention lies mainly in their flowers. Childhood recollections of lemon-scented leaves in the fingerbowls at dinner parties, of a rose geranium leaf in apple jelly, of the pleasant odor which arose from a plant by the doorstep when a skirt brushed its foliage, are memories which endear these plants to one through life.

There are mint and apple scents in different species, and many other pelargoniums within the group have well defined sweet, spicy, fruity, and pungent odors.

In addition to the fragrance of the leaves, this group is noted for its great variety of leaf shapes and patterns, such as bring delight to artists, architects, and designers. The texture of the leaves in different kinds adds further interest. One needs only to handle leaves of P. *fragrans*, P. *crispum*, P. *denticulatum*, P. *tomentosum* and P. *quercifolium* to appreciate the range of textures.

In a garden the low-growing P. *odoratissimum*, P. *fragrans* and P. *graveolens* 'Grey Lady Plymouth' are choice bushy plants for the border. If rambling types are more desirable, P. *capitatum* and its derivative 'Attar of Roses' will prove satisfactory. All of these emit fragrance when the foliage is touched or bruised. Large shrubby kinds for background planting include P. *denticulatum* and P. *radens* (formerly known as P. *radula*); since these branch freely and their

101

fernlike leaves are of good size, they provide interesting foliage for flower arrangements.

The flowers of this group are not as showy as those discussed in previous chapters, but they are not inconspicuous. A group of distinctive, mildly scented hybrids described on page 117 have flowers nearly as large and bright as *P. domesticum* and *P. fulgidum* from which they are derived through crossing with scented-leaved sorts. Among the species, the showiest flowers are those produced by *P. quercifolium* and some of its offspring. This is inclined to ramble but its derivative 'Fair Ellen' grows upright and bushy and is of medium height, the flowers are brighter, and in similarly large clusters.

Any classification of horticultural material can only be arbitrary. Since the size and appearance of a plant are of importance to the gardener, the groupings here are based mainly on height and form of leaf. Large pelargoniums with lobed leaves are treated on page 103 and those with feathery leaves on page 112. Small-leaved pelargoniums are generally smaller in size as well, so they are considered together on page 113, followed by the mildly scented hybrids previously mentioned. There will, of course, be overlapping types as well as variations within each group.

As an additional aid in identification, some of the more distinctive characteristics of the species are summarized here. *Pelargonium abrotanifolium* and much material of the hybrid *P. fragrans* have long-spurred flowers. The first, however, has finely pinnate leaves like those of southernwood (*Artemisia abrotanum*), the second has palmately nerved and shallowly lobed leaves.

The remaining species are all short-spurred. *Pelargonium tomentosum* is distinctive for its leaves that are densely white-hairy on the lower surface. *P. australe, P. grossularioides,* and *P. odoratissimum* have very small flowers with sepals one-fourth inch long or less and petals not more than three-eighths inch long. *P. australe* has a scarcely visible spur one-twelfth inch long or less. The other two have a spur one-sixth inch long or more but differ in flower color, *P. grossularioides* having deep red-purple petals, *P. odoratissimum* white or pale pink petals lined with red.

The numerous species with green leaves and petals one-half inch long or more are not as easy to separate. *P. crispum* stands alone in its small, three-lobed leaves with strongly crisped margins. *P. scabrum* has

deeply lobed leaves that are wedge-shaped at the base. Leaves of
P. *capitatum* and P. *vitifolium* are roundish in outline, very softly
hairy and bluntly lobed with the lobes not extending farther than the
middle of the blade.

Deeply lobed leaves with more or less heart-shaped bases are typical
of P. *quercifolium*, P. *glutinosum*, P. *denticulatum*, P. *graveolens* and
P. *radens*. The first two species have lobes that are not dissected,
merely minutely or at least simply toothed. In P. *quercifolium*, the
lobes are rounded as in many of the white oaks; in P. *glutinosum*
they are sharply pointed.

The last three not only have deeply lobed leaves but the lobes are
again lobed and toothed, becoming almost fernlike in P. *denticulatum*
and P. *radens*. A sticky, smooth upper surface distinguishes P. *denticulatum*. Harshly hairy, rasping leaves with the edges rolled under
signify P. *radens*. Soft-hairy, flat, less deeply cut leaves are the mark
of P. *graveolens*.

LARGE PLANTS WITH LOBED, SCENTED LEAVES

Well grown specimens in this arbitrarily designated group become
bushy in form and tall in stature. Among those that may reach a
height of four feet or more are P. *scabrum*, P. *glutinosum*, P. *viscosissimum*, and their derivatives. Slightly lower in stature is a group including five important and widely hybridized species. These, which
are treated below under their specific designations, are: P. *capitatum*
and the very similar P. *vitifolium*, also P. *tomentosum*, P. *quercifolium*, and P. *graveolens*. Some of these rank among the earliest of
pelargoniums brought into cultivation. They are favored in gardens
for their architectural beauty and for their pleasing fragrances. Plants
probably of hybrid origin and belonging to this group are often
erroneously named as P. *decipiens*, P. *dennisianum* or P. *melissinum*
although these old hybrids are not known to be cultivated in American gardens.

Some Bushlike Species and their Hybrids

P. *scabrum* (L.) L'Hér. ex Ait.—Shrubby, much branched, harshly
hairy and glandular, to four feet or more; leaves to two inches long,

wedge shaped at the base, deeply three- to five-lobed, the lobes deeply
cut and toothed, smooth above, harshly hairy on the veins and margins below; umbels numerous at the tips of branches, each with two
to six short-spurred rose or white flowers up to three-fourths inch long,
the upper petals striped and blotched with red. South African species
introduced into England in 1775. The true species is probably not in
cultivation. Plants given this name in America appear to be of unde-
termined hybrid origin and are often given the name *Pelargonium*
'M. Ninon.'

'**M. Ninon**'—Apricot-scented. Bushy, much branched, harsh-hairy,
glandular; stems strong, erect, to four feet or more; leaves large, triangular in outline, deeply three-lobed with the lobes again divided,
margins of all lobes coarsely toothed and curled; inflorescences axillary,
many flowered, the flowers small, white to deep pink or perhaps even
red, with carmine spot and purple veins on upper petals. The name
has not been traced in the literature but is associated with plants in
American gardens. Typographical variants such as 'Mrs. Nonin'; and
'Ninon' have been noted.

P. glutinosum (Jacq.) L'Hér. ex Ait [syns. *P. viscosum* (Cav.) Harv.
& Sond., *P. viscosum-glutinosum* Hort.]—Pungent-scented. Plants
bushy, much-branched, strong and erect, to four feet or more; leaves
large, to four inches long on short petioles, glandular-hairy and
clammy to the touch, often dark-colored about the main veins, triangular in outline, deeply five- to seven-lobed, the lobes triangular and sharply pointed with irregularly toothed margins; umbels
axillary, short, few-flowered, the small orchid pink to pink, short-
spurred flowers blotched and streaked with crimson on the upper
petals. Introduced into England about 1777 from South Africa and
grown in Europe. Illustrated in *Curtis's Botanical Magazine* t. 143
(1791) and as *Geranium viscosum* by Andrews in *Geraniums* t. 51.

'**Pheasants Foot**'—Sweetly pungent-scented. Similar to *P. glutinosum* in its habit but not as tall nor as densely branched; leaves
somewhat smaller on longer petioles, usually five-lobed, the lobes distant, linear-triangular or broad-linear, blunt at the base, margins
toothed; flowers similar to those of *P. glutinosum*. This may be what
Andrews described as a variety of *Geranium viscosum* in *Geraniums*,
t. 51. At least some of the plants called 'Pheasants Foot' are very
similar to the following old hybrid.

P. × *jatrophaefolium* DC.—A hybrid between *P. denticulatum* and *P. glutinosum* according to Knuth but said by De Candolle to be intermediate between *P. denticulatum* and *P. quercifolium* 'Pinnatifidum' with smooth, sticky, deeply lobed leaves having sharply pointed teeth; umbels about four-flowered.

P. viscosissimum Sweet—Habit of *P. glutinosum* but the leaves more deeply lobed, the lobes narrower and more strongly toothed; flowers short-spurred, five to eight in an umbel, the petals nearly equal, lilac or white streaked with red on the upper two. Illustrated by Sweet, t. 115, and thought to be a natural species raised from seed obtained in Cape Province, South Africa. Others have considered it a hybrid derived from *P. glutinosum.*

P. capitatum and its Relatives

P. capitatum (L.) L'Hér. ex Ait.—The "rose-scented storksbill" of ancestral English gardens. Habit of growth shrubby; stems rambling or lax, to three feet long or more, branching, hairy, densely leafy; leaves to three inches, light green, hairy, shallowly three-lobed, the lobes rounded and overlapping, margins toothed, undulate; flowers short-spurred, lavender pink, in dense clusters, the upper petals purple veined. Discovered in South Africa and introduced into England in 1690.

'Attar of Roses'—Rose-scented. Related to *P. capitatum* from which it differs in that the stems are somewhat shorter, leaves harsher on upper surfaces, flowers rose-pink, the upper petals more conspicuously purple veined. Introduced at the New York Botanical Garden from England, 1923.

'Elkhorn'—Rose-scented. Similar to *P. capitatum* in habit of growth but differs in following ways: leaves three-lobed but lobe at apex elongated, margins not as strongly toothed, flowers pink with more purple veining in upper petals. England, 1860's.

'Fringed Oak'—Of similar origin to 'Logees Snowflake' from which it differs in having smaller leaves that are three- to five-lobed, the depth of the lobes variable; flower clusters dense, flowers larger than those of *P. capitatum*, pink, the upper petals more conspicuously marked with purple.

'Godfrey's Pride'—Pungently mint-scented. Habit of growth large, shrubby, rangy; leaves large, green with yellow streaks in some, three-lobed, the margins sharply toothed; flowers pink with darker veining in upper petals. Origin obscure.

'Logees Snowflake'—Of similar origin to 'Round Leaf Rose' (below), which it resembles except that the green leaves are variously streaked with white.

'Major'—Mildly rose-scented. Habit of *P. capitatum*, differing in taller growth; leaves larger, margins not as sharply toothed; flowers similar in form but rose pink in color. Probably of hybrid origin. Veitch, England, 1879. Also called 'Large-leaved Rose.' Some plants that belong here are erroneously called *P. quinquevulnerum*.

'Round Leaf Rose'—Habit of *P. capitatum*, leaves somewhat similar in shape and lobing but more stiffly hairy, stems more lax; flowers small, lavender, in dense clusters. A chance seedling of *P. capitatum* × *P. quercifolium* raised in North Street Greenhouses, Danielson, Conn.

'Shrubland Pet' (syn. 'Shrubland Rose')—A hybrid of *P. capitatum* with a cross between a *P. quercifolium* hybrid or cultivar and *P. fulgidum*. Habit of growth vigorous, spreading, branching, the stems lax; leaves large, lobed somewhat like those of *P. capitatum*, glossy and sparsely bristly hairy above with purple area in center indicating a relationship to *P. quercifolium*; inflorescence intermediate in size, axillary, dense, the flowers rose red with more purple marking in upper petals. Mr. Beaton of Shrubland Park Nursery, England, devoted seven years to the development of this hybrid, which was distributed in 1849. He had hoped for brilliant coloring in the flowers from the *P. fulgidum* parent. Although his wish did not materialize, this hybrid is one of the most colorful in the group.

'Skeltons Unique'—Pungent-scented. A hybrid of *P. capitatum* and *P. quercifolium*. Vigorous with lax, branching stems not as densely leafy as in the first named parent; flower clusters dense, flowers intermediate in size, light pink, the upper petals purple marked like those of *P. quercifolium*. Originated in England about 1861.

P. × *concolor* Sweet—A hybrid of *P. capitatum* and *P.* × *ignescens* (an old *P. fulgidum* hybrid); habit of growth shrubby, branching, spreading, the stems and branches erect or lax, shaggy hairy, densely leafy; leaves small, to about two inches, softly hairy, heart-shaped in outline, three- to five-lobed, the margins toothed; umbels axillary, numerous, extending beyond the foliage, six- to eight-flowered, the flowers bright red or orangy scarlet with dark lines and splotches on the upper petals, the spur longer than the calyx. Originated in England about 1820 and illustrated by Sweet. t. 140.

Plants grown in American gardens under the name *P. concolor* seem to be of the same general parentage but the leaves are more deeply divided and lacy, showing a stronger influence of *P. fulgidum*. Although the name 'Shotesham Pet' has been used erroneously for both these plants, the real 'Shotesham Pet' was originated in England about 1858 from entirely different parentage. To distinguish the plant known in America and a lavender-flowered form of it from the plant illustrated by Sweet, the following names are proposed:

'Concolor Lace'—Mildly filbert-scented. Similar in habit to *P. concolor* but the leaves light green, softly hairy, thin, ovate in outline, pinnate or pinnatifid, five- to seven-lobed, lobes more or less wedge-shaped at base, margins of segments incised and toothed; umbels axillary, numerous, extending beyond the foliage; flowers five to seven in each umbel, crimson with darker veins in upper petals.

'Lavender Lace'—This name is here proposed for another plant that is usually listed as 'Shotesham Pet' and to which it is not related. It is similar to 'Concolor Lace' in all respects except for the color of the flowers, which is lavender. This variation may be a reversion to the flower color of *P. capitatum*.

P. vitifolium (L.) L'Hér. ex Ait.—Similar to *P. capitatum* and difficult to distinguish, though more erect with larger and more clearly three-lobed leaves with harsher hairs. Although said to be scented in South Africa it is sometimes scentless here. Harvey kept it as a separate species mainly because it dated back to Linnaeus and Dillenius, having been cultivated in England as early as 1724.

P. tomentosum and Derivatives

P. tomentosum Jacq.—Mint-scented. Habit bushy; stems erect, to three feet tall, branching, densely soft white-hairy; leaves numerous, broadly ovate or triangular heart-shaped in outline, green but with a feltlike covering of white hairs, shallowly three- to seven-lobed, the margins scalloped and toothed; inflorescence branched with several umbels of small white or tinted white, short-spurred flowers, the petals narrow, the upper deeper tinged at base. Discovered in South

Africa and introduced into England before 1700. Illustrated in *Curtis's Botanical Magazine* t. 518 (1801) and by Sweet, t. 168.

'Joy Lucille'—Mint-scented. A hybrid of *P. graveolens* and *P. tomentosum*; habit of growth loose and rangy; leaves large, green, feltlike white-hairy, three-lobed, all lobes scalloped and toothed; flowers small, pink with carmine marking in upper petals. Logee, Connecticut, 1940's.

'Robers Lemon Rose' (syns. 'Canadian Silver Seedling,' 'Western Rose Seedling')—Spicy rose-scented. A hybrid of *P. graveolens* and *P. tomentosum*; habit of growth shrubby, stems erect, to two feet or more, branching, not densely leafy; leaves intermediate in size, to two inches long and as broad across the base, triangular in outline, pinnatifid to pinnate, the segments irregularly lobed and toothed, feltlike white-hairy; flower clusters dense, flowers pink, the upper petals crimson veined. Rober, California, 1940's. This hybrid is now grown commercially in California for its volatile oil.

Two unnamed hybrids are being grown under their parental names *denticulatum* × *tomentosum*; the proposed names for these plants and their descriptions are as follows:

'Mopsy'—Shrubby, branching, soft white-hairy, stems erect, to a foot or more; leaves more or less triangular in outline, an inch and a half long or slightly more and as broad across the base, pinnately five-lobed, the lobes distant, basal lobes again divided but not as deeply, segments linear and rounded at apex, margins coarsely toothed, gray-green, feltlike white-hairy, leaf-pattern uniform; inflorescence intermediate in form; petals long, pale pink, the upper ones carmine-feathered. Origin obscure.

'Topsy'—Mint-scented. Habit of growth bushy, stems erect, to three feet or more, branching, softly white-hairy throughout; petiole equal to the leaf-blade in length, leaves large, to three and one half inches or more, broadly triangular heart-shaped, pinnately seven-lobed, felt-like, the margins of all segments coarsely toothed and curled; inflorescence intermediate, the petals pale pink. Introduced at the New York Botanical Garden from Kew Gardens, England.

P. quercifolium and Derivatives

P. quercifolium (L.f.) L'Hér. ex Ait.—Pungent-scented. Shrubby, stocky, rough hairy with branching, erect, or tortuous stems to three

feet or more; leaves numerous, dark green, brown purple along midrib
and main veins, to two inches long and about as broad at the base,
roughly resembling oak leaves in shape, pinnately five-lobed, the
basal lobes widely separated from the upper ones, all the lobes
rounded at the tip, glossy and sparsely bristly hairy above; numerous
short-stalked axillary umbels bear three to seven large rose pink,
short-spurred flowers having upper petals with a conspicuous dark
purple spot and feathering, the lower petals paler. Showy. This is the
true "Oak Geranium" introduced from South Africa to England in
1774. A number of forms and hybrids are cultivated under fancy
names.

'Beauty Oak'—A chance hybrid of *P. quercifolium* 'Giganteum' and
P. tomentosum with rangy, branching stems; leaves long-petioled,
rounded heart-shaped in outline, three- to five-lobed, the margins of
lobes and lobules sharply toothed, center of light green leaf marked
with characteristic brown-purple; inflorescence branched as in *P.
tomentosum* with numerous umbels on slender stalks; flowers small,
similar to those of *P. tomentosum* in size and form, rosy lavender
with purple feathering in upper petals. Originated in Connecticut.

'Carlton Oak'—A hybrid of *P. denticulatum* 'Filicifolium' and
P. quercifolium, resembling *P. quercifolium* in habit; leaves bright
green, not as harshly hairy, about two and one half inches long,
similarly lobed except that the upper lobe is again divided into three
and the purple coloring is evident only in the main veins; flowers
small with a dark spot on the upper petals. Arndt, 1950.

'Fair Ellen'—Pungent-scented. Habit of *P. quercifolium*, the stems
erect, more branched and not quite as tall; leaves similar to those of
the species; flowers somewhat larger, bright magenta-pink with larger
purple spot in upper petals Floriferous and handsome. Originated in
England, 1840's.

'Giganteum'—Pungent-scented. Differs from the species in larger
size; leaves twice as large or more, usually five-lobed, broader, not as
blunt across the base; flowers slightly smaller with smaller dark spot
on upper petals. England, 1850.

'Haviland'—Pungent-scented. Similar to 'Giganteum' except that
the brown-purple area is larger and more conspicuous. Arndt, 1947.

'Pinnatifidum'—Differs from the species in that the primary lobes are
again lobed. Originally illustrated by L'Héritier, t. 15, but not recognized as a wild variety.

'Pretty Polly'—Mildly pungent-scented. A multiple hybrid derived in part from *P. quercifolium* with characteristic brown or black-purple area in the center of the leaves. The short, thick, woody stems branch at the top and reach a height of a foot; leaves numerous, arising in tufts at the ends of stems and branches, bright green, thinner in texture than others of this group, triangular heart-shaped and deeply three-lobed, the primary lobes deeply divided and the margins sharply toothed; flowers rarely produced but reported to be pink with upper petals ornamented with maroon-red. Originated in England about 1850.

'Prostratum'—A small prostrate form of *P. quercifolium* with smaller leaves but similar flowers.

'Staghorn'—Pungent-scented. Similar to *P. quercifolium* in habit of growth; leaves of like size and outline but differing in that each segment has an additional round lobe suggesting incipient antlers about to emerge from a stag's horn. In some leaves the terminal lobe is elongated with seven to nine lobules; inflorescence similar to that of the species. England, about 1860.

'Village Hill Oak'—Pungent-scented. Habit of growth like that of *P. quercifolium;* leaves sometimes broader, five- to seven-lobed, lower division of the basal lobes pointing downward, all segments furnished with rounded and pointed lobes; flowers more densely clustered, smaller and paler with smaller dark spot on upper petals. A hybrid of *P. quercifolium* raised at Village Hill Nursery, Massachusetts.

P. graveolens and Derivatives

P. graveolens L'Hér. ex Ait.—Rose-scented. Habit of growth bushy, the stems erect, to three feet or more, soft short-hairy throughout, branching, densely leafy; leaves an inch and a half long or more on slightly shorter petioles, the blade triangular in outline with a more or less heart-shaped base, deeply five-lobed almost in pinnate fashion, the lobes broad-linear and rounded at the toothed margins, the soft white hairs on the upper surface making the blades appear gray-green; umbels short-stalked, axillary, densely five- to ten-flowered; flowers short-spurred, pink to rose pink with purple veins and spots on upper petals. Familiarly known as the "Rose Geranium," native in South Africa and introduced into England, 1774. It or hybrids derived from it are now extensively grown in southern Europe for rose-geranium oil used for perfumes. The name *P. terebinthinaceum* is sometimes used incorrectly for *P. graveolens* or for 'Little Gem.'

'Camphor Rose'—Camphor-scented. Similar to the species itself in habit of growth but coarser throughout; leaves larger and bristly-hairy; inflorescence similar but the flowers rose pink. Originated fifty or more years ago. The name *P. graveolens* var. *camphorum* is also used but it does not represent a botanical variety.

'Granelous'—Rose-scented. Similar to *P. graveolens* but coarser throughout; leaves variable, some longer than in the species, the segments wedge-shaped rather than linear, rounded at the ends, more deeply lobed and more coarsely toothed; flowers similar to those of the species. Origin obscure.

'Grey Lady Plymouth'—Rose-scented. Stems vigorous, lax, spreading, otherwise similar to *P. graveolens*; leaves more regularly lobed and toothed than in the species, gray-green, soft white-hairy, with a narrow white line around the edge; flowers like those of the species.

'Lady Plymouth'—Rose-scented. A lower growing and less vigorous form of *P. graveolens*; leaves green, blotched with creamy white; flowers similar to those of the species. Described in English literature, 1852, as "a diminutive mutant of *P. graveolens*."

'Little Gem'—Sweet-scented. A hybrid derivative of *P. graveolens*, similar to the species but not as tall; leaves more lobed and toothed; flowers rose-pink with two purple lines in upper petals. Originated in England in the 1860's.

'Minor'—Rose-scented. similar to the species but smaller in all its parts; flowers similar except that they are proportionately smaller and deeper in color.

'Mrs. Taylor'—Almost devoid of scent. Habit of growth similar to that of *P. graveolens*, the stems erect but not as much branched; leaves to four inches, smaller in old plants, ovate or nearly triangular in outline, usually heart-shaped at base, five- to seven-lobed, the basal lobes parted almost all the way to the midrib, the major lobes divided into lesser lobes of various depths, the margins lobulate and coarsely toothed, ruffled or flat; umbels axillary, extending beyond the foliage; flowers short-spurred, large, not crowded, scarlet, crimson, or vermilion, the upper petals ornamented with very deep purple red.

Known since 1884 and arising spontaneously from time to time. It is often grown under the following erroneous names: *P. atrum, P. coccineum, P. filtrum, P. hybridum.*

'Red-Flowered Rose'—Almost devoid of scent. Habit of growth similar to that of *P. graveolens* but not as tall; leaves larger and not as symmetrical in lobing, the lobes wedge-shaped, variable; flowers larger, cerise, the upper petals darker with black-red spot. The color and size of the flowers indicate a relationship to *P. fulgidum.*

P. × *blandfordianum* (Andr.) Sweet—Slightly pungent-scented. Presumed to be a hybrid of *P. graveolens* crossed with *P. echinatum;* plants not as erect or as tall as *P. graveolens,* softly white-hairy throughout and with more slender stems; leaves more deeply divided than those of *P. graveolens,* especially on the upper parts of the stems, segments much narrower, gray-green; umbels more loosely flowered, the white or pale blush flowers veined with purple and splotched with red on the two upper petals. England, 1818. Illustrated by Sweet, t. 101.

LARGE PLANTS WITH FEATHERY, SCENTED LEAVES

In the present classification the three species treated immediately below and their related cultivars are distinguished from the larger group immediately preceding by the narrow segments which give the leaves a feathery or lacy effect. Two of the species are capable of reaching great size; the third, *P. abrotanifolium,* seldom exceeds two feet in height.

P. denticulatum Jacq.—Pungent-scented. Shrubby, much-branched, with clammy stems; leaves to two inches, pinnately and deeply lobed, the lobes again pinnately toothed, the upper surface smooth, sticky, flat, the margins not rolled under; umbels with one to three short-spurred, lilac or pink flowers, the upper petals spotted and veined with purple and notched at the tip. Native in South Africa and introduced into England, 1789. Illustrated by Sweet, t. 109. Much of the *P. denticulatum* grown in America is erroneously identified and is actually *P. radens* or one of its derivatives.

'Carlton Fern' [*P. denticulatum* 'Filicifolium' × *P. quercifolium*]—Habit of *P. denticulatum* 'Filicifolium' but with larger leaves having segments about as broad but more numerous; flowers similar to those of *P. denticulatum.* Arndt, 1950.

'Filicifolium' (syn. *P. filicifolium* Hort.)—Pungent-scented. A form of *P. denticulatum* with very finely cut leaves, lacy in appearance. The earliest reference to this cultivar was found in a catalog issued by the Henderson firm in England, 1879.

P. radens H. E. Moore [syn. *P. radula* (Cav.) L'Hér. ex Ait.]— Rose-scented. Shrubby with erect branching stems up to four feet high, the young growth softly hairy; leaves more or less triangular to heart-shaped in general outline, deeply pinnately lobed, the lobes again pinnately toothed, the upper surface covered with short, harsh, rasping hairs, the margins rolled under; umbels axillary, short-stalked, about five-flowered, the short-spurred flowers soft pink with purple veins and splotches on the entire-margined upper petals. Introduced into England from South Africa about 1774. Material called *P. denticulatum* 'Dr. Livingston,' *P. graveolens* 'Dr. Livingston,' and 'Skeleton Rose' belongs to this species.

'Carlton Corsage' [*P. capitatum* × *P. radens*]—Rose- and mint-scented. Habit of *P. radens* which it resembles except that the leaves are larger, the segments so numerous that they overlap, giving a very full and ruffled effect. Named for its popularity as a corsage foliage. Arndt, 1949.

P. abrotanifolium (L.f.) Jacq.—Aromatic-scented. Stems erect, to about two feet, slender, woody, densely branching; leaves to an inch long with very tiny stipules, velvety white-hairy, three-parted, each part divided into very narrow, linear, channeled, blunt lobes; umbels of one to four long-spurred white or sometimes colored flowers, the upper petals pink flushed and marked with a red spot in white-flowered plants. The leaf arrangement along the stem suggests ruffled tufts of sheer lace held aloft by thin wire. Introduced into England from Cape Colony, 1796. Illustrated by Sweet, t. 351. A somewhat similar but scentless species is grown by fanciers under the name *P. divaricatum*. It does not altogether agree with Knuth's description of *P. divaricatum*. Considerable study will be necessary to classify this plant properly.

SMALL-LEAVED SCENTED PELARGONIUMS

Plants as well as leaves are generally of lesser size in this group of scented-leaved species and hybrids. Here will be found *P. crispum* and *P. odoratissimum*, their relatives and hybrid offspring, as well as

two species which are still known apparently only in their original
wild form.

P. crispum, its Derivatives and Relatives

P. crispum (L.) L'Hér. ex Ait.—Lemon-scented. A small shrub to
three feet high with rigidly erect stems and branches; leaves obtusely
heart-shaped or kidney-shaped, to one and one-half inches long, often
on short petioles, smooth or very slightly hairy, shallowly three-
lobed, the margins finely toothed and crisped; umbels one- to three-
flowered, the short-spurred flowers lavender, washed with purple and
brightly veined on the upper petals. Introduced into England from
South Africa, 1774. Illustrated by Sweet, t. 383.

'French Lace'—Lemon-scented. Habit of *P. crispum* but bushier
and of more rapid growth, similarly pyramidal in shape; leaves green
with white margins. Distinctive and well named. Arndt, 1948.

'Lady Mary'—Mildly lemon-scented. Similar to *P. citrosum* in habit
of growth; the leaves differ in being more obviously hairy, often
shallowly round-lobed, usually squared at the base, the margins
coarsely toothed; flowers larger and more brightly colored, the upper
petals feathered and blotched, the lower pale. Originated in England
and perhaps the same as the early hybrid *P. limoneum* illustrated by
Sweet as t. 278.

'Latifolium'—Habit of growth looser than that of *P. crispum* itself;
leaves nearly twice as large as usual and more distantly placed on
stem; umbels on long slender stalks.

'Minus' (syn. 'Minor')—Lemon-scented. Similar to *P. crispum* but
differs in the very small leaves so closely attached to the stems that
they are scarcely apparent; flowers smaller and paler. Sometimes
known as *P. hospes* Hoffmsgg. but not definitely identified with it.

'Prince of Orange'—A large form with broad leaves to nearly two
inches, the blades nearly flat and not as strongly crisped as in *P. crispum*; flowers lavender to lavender pink, the upper petals feathered
dark red. Originated in England before 1850 and named for the
orange scent of the leaves.

'Prince Rupert'—Lemon-scented. Similar to *P. crispum* but differs
in the larger leaves and shorter petioles; flowers of the same color, the
upper petals carmine-veined. A variegated form is sometimes given
the name 'Variegated Prince Rupert.'

'Variegatum'—Lemon-scented. Similar to the species except that the leaves are variegated green and white. This is often erroneously called *P. grossularioides*.

P. × *citrosum* Voigt ex Sprague [syns. *P.* × *citriodorum* Schrank, not *P. citriodorum* (Cav.) Mart.]—Lemon-scented. Small and spreading with erect or sometimes lax stems; leaves small, to an inch or more, broadly ovate, obtuse or rounded at the base, pointed at the tip, the margins irregularly shallow-lobed, sharply toothed and incised; umbels two- to four-flowered, the pale rose flowers darkly feathered with red on the upper petals. A number of different forms were called *Geranium citriodorum* by Andrews in *Geraniums*, (1805) but unfortunately the name was improper and technically the name *P. citrosum* must be used. The plants often known in American gardens as *P. citriodorum* 'Prince of Orange' are listed above simply as 'Prince of Orange.'

P. × *nervosum* Sweet—Lime-scented. Habit similar to that of *P. crispum*; leaves rounded or kidney-shaped, to an inch and a half long, blunt at the base, glossy dark green, margins sharply toothed but usually unlobed; flowers lavender with bright feathering in upper petals. Raised by Dennis in England about 1820. Illustrated by Sweet, t. 47.

'Toronto'—Aromatic-scented. A modern hybrid of obscure origin, perhaps remotely derived from *P. crispum* but similar to *P. nervosum* in habit; leaves lighter green, larger than those of *P. nervosum* but similar in shape; umbel with four or more larger, rosy lavender flowers with darker markings on upper petals.

P. × *scarboroviae* Sweet (syns. 'Countess of Scarborough,' 'Limoneum Strawberry')—Sweet-scented. Stems to a foot tall, lax, densely branched; leaves to an inch or slightly more, glossy dark green, rigid, three-lobed with the central lobe usually three-parted, the margins toothed, incised and crisped; flowers large with a rather long spur, bright purplish red, feathered in red on the upper petals, the lower petals pale lilac or stained with red. Illustrated by Sweet, t. 117.

P. odoratissimum and its Relatives and Hybrids

P. odoratissimum (L.) L'Hér. ex Ait.—Sweetly apple-scented. Habit of growth low, bushy, spreading; leaves to an inch and a half or more, bright green, like finest silk velvet to the touch, ovate, heart-shaped at base, the margins shallowly round-lobed, coarsely toothed and ruffled; inflorescence branched into numerous few-flowered umbels; flowers small, usually less than half an inch long with a short spur and white petals, the upper ones spotted and veined with red. Native in South Africa. Cultivated in England, 1724. Illustrated by Sweet, t. 299. A variegated form of *P. odoratissimum* arises spontaneously from time to time.

P. × *fragrans* Willd.—Thought to be a hybrid between *P. exstipulatum* and *P. odoratissimum*; habit of growth similar to *P. odoratissimum* except that the leaves are smaller, to slightly more than an inch, similarly soft hairy but extremely variable in shape and outline —some leaves like those of *P. crispum*, others like those of *P. citrosum*, the leaves at base of flowering branches often crenately lobed and toothed; flowers small with an often reddish spur up to twice as long as the sepals, the petals white, tinged red on the upper two. Originated in the Berlin Botanical Garden about 1793. Illustrated by Willdenow in *Hortus Berolinensis* t. 77 (1816) and by Sweet, t. 172. Several different scents of spicy fragrance are available through the hybridizing efforts of M. H. Arndt. Has been listed by the erroneous name *P. turpintha*.

'Codys Fragrans'—Aromatic-scented. Similar to *P. fragrans* except that it grows more compactly, the leaves are lighter green, larger, and usually kidney-shaped. Originated in New England.

'Logee'—Sweetly aromatic-scented. A hybrid of *P. fragrans* and *P. odoratissimum* similar to the latter in growth but differing in the erratically lobed leaves with handsomely ruffled margins; flowers like those of *P. fragrans*. Originated by Ernest Logee in Connecticut about 1948.

Other Small-Leaved Species

P. australe Willd.—Short-stemmed with usually several slender, erect, softly hairy herbaceous branches to one foot high; leaves to one and a half inches long, heart-shaped with rounded tip and with scalloped, sometimes shallowly lobed margin, softly hairy on both sides; umbels axillary with six to twenty-five densely crowded flowers having a scarcely perceptible spur, small hairy sepals and narrow white to rose petals less than half an inch long, the upper two spotted and streaked with carmine. A native of Australia introduced into England in 1792. Illustrated by Sweet, t. 68. The plants cultivated by this name in America may be a derivative of *P. capitatum.*

P. grossularioides (L.) L'Hér. ex Ait.—Sweet-scented. Herbaceous with slender stems reclining at the base; leaves long-petioled, to an inch and a half, softly hairy, round heart-shaped with closely toothed, scalloped-lobed margins resembling those of a gooseberry; umbels dense with very many small, short-spurred, purplish red flowers less than one-fourth inch long. A native of South Africa cultivated as early as 1731 by Philip Miller in England and naturalized in California. It is often erroneously called *P. parviflorum.* Plants of *P. crispum* 'Variegatum' have been miscalled *P. grossularioides.*

DISTINCTIVE, MILDLY SCENTED PELARGONIUMS

Showy flowers and large habit showing the influence of *P. domesticum* and *P. fulgidum* are characteristic of this last group. Although they are usually listed with other scented-leaved species their fragrance is milder and at times may be scarcely perceptible.

'California Brilliant'—A hybrid or mutant similar to *P. domesticum* in habit of growth; leaves round, heart-shaped at base, shallowly lobed with regularly and sharply toothed margins; flowers cherry red, paling toward the center. This modern plant is often known simply as 'Brilliant.' The substitute name 'California Brilliant' is suggested to avoid confusion with other pelargoniums also known as 'Brilliant' that originated at an earlier period.

'Capri'—A modern chance hybrid of *P. domesticum* which it resembles in habit of growth; leaves variable, usually three-lobed, blunt or heart-shaped at the base with coarsely toothed and undulate margins; umbels axillary, few-flowered, the flowers slightly larger than those of 'Scarlet Unique' and equally brilliant in color. Variations in flower color have been noted in different plants raised from seed of 'Capri,' these colors ranging from orchid pink and rose pink to scarlet and vermilion.

'Cerise Unique'—Similar to 'Scarlet Unique' (below) except that the flowers are cerise-crimson. Originated in England about 1860.

'Clorinda' [*P. domesticum* × *P. quercifolium*]—Plants with habit of *P. domesticum*; leaves large, three-lobed, the lobes rounded with toothed margins; flower clusters large and showy, the flowers large, rose red, upper petals tinged violet. Cannell & Son, England, before 1900. A mutant of 'Clorinda' with orchid-colored flowers is called 'Orchid Clorinda.'

'Mrs. Kingsley'—Small, shrubby and compact; leaves somewhat like those of 'Rollisons Unique' except that they are smaller and more densely hairy, the margins ruffled and more coarsely toothed, petioles relatively shorter; inflorescence similar to 'Rollisons Unique' in form and color. Originated in England. Often known erroneously as 'Mrs. Kingsbury' or as *P. rapaceum.*

'Rollisons Unique'—Habit of growth similar to that of 'Scarlet Unique': leaves are as large but rounder in outline, more coarsely hairy and with lobes similarly rounded but the margins more sharply toothed; inflorescence similar except that the flowers are crimson with purple dendritic marks in the upper petals. Distributed by Rollison in England about 1850 but said to have originated in South Ireland many years before.

'Scarlet Unique'—Herbaceous, stems to five feet tall, green, succulent-woody, softly hairy when young, lax with few branches; leaves ovate in outline, heart-shaped at base, seven-lobed, the lobes rounded with irregularly crenate, ruffled margins, silky short white-hairy but not as silvery as in the species *P. fulgidum;* inflorescence medium-tall, axillary, the flowers large, brilliant scarlet, the upper petals feathered deep purple. Resembles *P. fulgidum,* from which it is largely derived. Originated in England more than a century ago.

Chapter 5

RARE AND UNUSUAL PELARGONIUMS

In addition to the more popular pelargoniums described in previous chapters, there are various species and hybrids, including the parental types of *P. domesticum* and *P. hortorum*, that are grown primarily by specialists and in botanical gardens. Among these are the aristocrats, the oddities, and curiosities: hybrids with flowers so dark that they are referred to as "black-flowered pelargoniums"; a group with brilliant flowers; deciduous and succulent plants, some with thickened or gouty looking nodes, others with dwarf gnarled stems or with cactus-like spines.

Although some of the unusual and rare pelargoniums demand special cultural attention, there are many that are not difficult to grow. Among those suitable for the house are *P. frutetorum* and *P. salmoneum*, relatives of the garden geraniums, with distinctive leaves and bright flowers. *Pelargonium cordifolium*, recently introduced, grows so large that it is more suitable for the open ground or in a pot on terrace or patio. Useful both indoors and out is the purple-flowered *P. reniforme*, which has a branching inflorescence sometimes reaching a considerable length. Northern gardeners may want to test the hardiness of *P. endlicherianum*, a herbaceous species with bright pink blossoms sweetly scented.

On the other hand, *P. tetragonum, P. gibbosum, P. stapletonii,* and other more succulent species are deciduous plants which shed their foliage, leaving the stems bare during their resting months. This habit excludes them for growing in the house where year-round leafy sub-jects are more desirable.

Still other species are known only from the wild state or are found occasionally in European or African botanical gardens but are rare in the United States. Yet to be introduced are such striking novelties as *P. bowkeri* with its fringed petals, yellow-flowered *P. triste*—one of the parents of *P. glaucifolium*, the related *P. lobatum* with its dull purple, evening-scented flowers, also the bizarre *P. squarrosum* and *P. xerophyton*, and *P. multibracteatum* from tropical Africa. The singular *P. cotyledonis* from the island of St. Helena, with its nearly regular white flowers and wrinkled leaves is under cultivation but rare.

The botanist arranges the wild species of *Pelargonium* in fifteen sections or groups of species. The smaller number considered in this chapter, however, is divided into fewer groups. All those species having large, woody, tuberous roots are placed together as Tuberous-Rooted Pelargoniums (page 120); the remainder having branched fibrous roots—Fibrous-Rooted Pelargoniums (page 124)—are sub-divided into Short-Spurred Pelargoniums (Page 124) and Long-Spurred Pelargoniums (page 128). Among the short-spurred species are some low ones with thick stems (page 124) and others that are tall and shrubby with slender stems (page 126). The long-spurred species are more varied and include some with very short lower petals (page 128), and others which may be arbitrarily classified by the nature of the foliage. There are some with leaves white-hairy on the underside (page 129), others with green leaves which are either deeply lobed and sharply toothed (page 130) or shallowly lobed and round-toothed (page 132).

TUBEROUS-ROOTED PELARGONIUMS

The tuberous-rooted pelargoniums cultivated in America have pinnately divided leaves and long-spurred flowers. A number of inter-esting species and hybrids are grown. *P. pinnatum* and *P. rapaceum* never develop stems and have their flower-clusters borne on stalks from the crown. The rest have at least a short perennial stem and bear the flower-clusters on annual herbaceous branches. Many of these are scented in the evening and have flowers in a range of colors. One species, *P. bowkeri* has fringed petals. Yellow or yellow-green flowers are found in *P. bowkeri*, *P. triste* and *P. gibbosum*, bright scarlet in

P. fulgidum, deep maroon, purple or nearly black flowers sometimes edged with yellow-green in *P. apiifolium, P. ardens, P. bicolor, P. glaucifolium, P. lobatum, P. quinquevulnerum, P. multiradiatum* and *P. rutaceum.*

P. apiifolium Jacq. f.—Stems short and thick with slender, hairy flowering branches; leaves smooth and glaucous, pinnately divided with stalked, wedge-shaped, again pinnately divided leaflets; inflorescence simple with numerous flowers, the spur several times as long as the sepals, the petals dark purple and pale margined. Perhaps a hybrid, cultivated since about 1800 in Europe but unknown in the wild. Deciduous.

P. × ardens Lodd.—A deciduous hybrid of *P. fulgidum* and *P. lobatum;* stems thick, knobby, short, fleshy-woody; branches few and stubby; leaves large, to eight inches or more, hairy, oblong-ovate, lobes variable, usually three to five, primary lobes furnished with blunt, coarsely toothed secondary ones; flowers large, in few-flowered umbels, scarlet with dark red spots on upper petals. Originated in England early in the 19th century. Illustrated by Sweet, t. 45. Deciduous.

P. bicolor (Jacq.) L'Hér. ex Ait.—Stems erect, to a foot and a half or more tall, the branches thickened at nodes; leaves thin, softly white-hairy, ovate or broadly heart-shaped in general outline, pinnately five- to seven-lobed, the lobes rounded with coarsely toothed, ciliate margins; inflorescence tall, axillary, the umbels containing numerous deep purple flowers with a spur twice as long as sepals and pale-margined petals. Known in cultivation since 1776 but not found in the wild and perhaps a hybrid. Illustrated by Sweet, t. 97.

P. bowkeri Harvey—Tubers large; stem very short; leaves to one foot long, compoundly pinnate with very slender segments, slightly hairy; umbels twelve- to eighteen-flowered on a stalk a foot or more high, the spur several times as long as the recurved sepals, the yellowish, nearly equal petals tinged with purple and deeply fringed. Native in Natal and Orange Free States, South Africa. Illustrated in *Curtis's Botanical Magazine* t. 5421 (1864). Grown at Kew Gardens. Not presently cultivated in America.

P. fulgidum (L.) L'Hér. ex Ait.—Stems thick, short, succulent-woody, densely pubescent with few deciduous branches; leaves to about four inches long, thin, soft silky silvery hairy on both sides, ovate in outline, pinnately three-lobed, the lower segments stalked and all segments as long as the apices are broad, margins irregularly round-lobed; inflorescence medium tall, often branched, with umbels of numerous large brilliant red flowers streaked with dark red or nearly black veins on the upper petals, the spur several times as long as the sepals and swollen at the top. Native in sandy soils in western Cape Province, South Africa. Introduced into England before 1732. Illustrated by Sweet, t. 69.

From earliest times this species was used in the development of hybrids and is one of the primal parents of the red-flowered forms in the *P. domesticum* group. Its effect may also be seen in some of the scented-leaved clones such as 'Capri,' 'Mrs. Kingsley,' 'Mrs. Taylor,' 'Red-flowered Rose,' 'Shrubland Pet,' and perhaps others.

P. gibbosum (L.) L'Hér. ex Ait.—Stems up to three feet tall, thick, fleshy-woody, much swollen in irregular fashion at the nodes, little branched; glaucous, nearly smooth, fleshy leaves rise in crownlike fashion from the upper part of stems and branches, the blades about three inches long, pinnately lobed with three to seven wedge-shaped, toothed, wrinkled segments sometimes borne on short stalks and often widely separated; umbels from the axils, many-flowered, the flowers greenish-yellow with a spur several times as long as the sepals. Native in Cape Province, South Africa and introduced into England in 1712 where it became known as the "Gouty Geranium" because of the swollen nodes. Illustrated by Sweet, t. 61. Deciduous.

P. × glaucifolium Sweet—An early hybrid of *P. gibbosum* and *P. lobatum*, rather like *P. gibbosum* but hairy with longer, glaucous, three- to five-lobed leaves and inflorescence of medium height with many dark maroon flowers having greenish yellow margins on the petals. Often called the "Black-flowered Pelargonium." Originated in England before 1823. Illustrated by Sweet, t. 179.

P. lobatum (L.) L'Hér. ex Ait.—Tubers large; stem short-branched; leaves large, to a foot long and broad, softly white-hairy, variable in shape and lobing, often three-lobed, the margins incised and doubly toothed; inflorescence of one or more long-stalked umbels, the flowers aromatic in the evening, dull purple with pale margins, the spur much longer than the sepals. Native in Cape Colony, South Africa. Cultivated in Chelsea Garden, England, 1739. Illustrated by Sweet, t. 51. Deciduous.

P. multiradiatum Wendl.—Stems short, thick; flowering branches leafy, thickened at nodes; leaves twice pinnate, hairy; flowers scented, numerous, the blackish petals margined with greenish yellow, the spur several times as long as sepals. Known only from cultivation and perhaps a hybrid derived from *P. lobatum*. Illustrated by Sweet, t. 145. Deciduous.

P. *pinnatum* (L.) L'Hér. ex Ait.—Tubers large, round or elongated; stems not developed; leaves on long hairy petioles, the blades rather thin, small, pinnate with few to many ovate leaflets, softly hairy; inflorescence to a foot tall, the flowers with light flesh to buff petals, the upper ones spotted and streaked with carmine, the spur more than twice as long as the sepals. Introduced into England from South Africa in 1788. Illustrated by Sweet, t. 46, as *Dimacria pinnata*. This species was introduced to the United States as P. *squarrosum*, a species of South Africa not known in cultivation and to which it bears no resemblance. Deciduous.

P. × *quinquevulnerum* (Andr.) Pers.—An old hybrid between P. *bicolor* and P. *triste*, much like the latter but the leaves not as uniformly divided or feathery; flowers scented, velvety purple with pale margins. Illustrated by Sweet, t. 161. Plants so named in gardens today are more likely to be derivatives of P. *capitatum*. Deciduous.

P. *rapaceum* (L.) L'Hér ex Ait.—Tubers rounded or elongate; stems not developed; leaves clustered at the crown with long, hairy petioles and small, softly hairy blades to eight inches long, twice pinnately divided into linear segments; inflorescence rising from the crown, to a foot high, bearing one or more densely many-flowered umbels of small, almost pealike flowers which are nearly sessile with a slender spur up to one and three-fourths inches long and recurved sepals about one-third inch long; the flowers vary from flesh pink to creamy yellow and have the upper petals streaked with carmine and bent backward, the lower petals broader, straight, and held close together. Color forms have sometimes been considered distinct varieties. Native on dry, stony mountainsides near Capetown, South Africa. Cultivated in England, 1701. Illustrated by Sweet, t. 18, as *Hoarea corydaliflora* and t. 135 as *Hoarea carinata*. Deciduous.

The quite different hybrid clone *Pelargonium* 'Mrs. Kingsley' described on page 118 is sometimes sold as P. *rapaceum* in the United States but the species itself is apparently cultivated only in private collections.

P. × *rutaceum* Sweet—An early hybrid of P. *gibbosum* and P. *multiradiatum*; stems thickened as in P. *gibbosum* but the larger hairy leaves much more deeply divided, the more numerous segments again pinnately cut and toothed; inflorescence tall with many dark maroon flowers, the base of upper petals and margins of all petals greenish-yellow; fragrant at night, the flowers and leaves said to smell like rue. Originated in England in 1823 and, like *P. glaucifolium*, known as "Black-flowered Pelargonium." Illustrated by Sweet, t. 279. Deciduous.

P. triste (L.) L'Hér. ex Ait.—Tuber about the size of a small potato; stems short, thick, fleshy, hairy; leaves large, to a foot long, three times pinnately divided and very feathery, the margins of segments laciniate, toothed, and hairy; inflorescence a tall, many-flowered umbel of brownish flowers with yellow margins, the spur much longer than the sepals. Native in clay soils in Cape Colony, South Africa. Known to English herbalists before 1600. Not presently in cultivation.

FIBROUS-ROOTED PELARGONIUMS

Most pelargoniums have fibrous roots although occasionally thickened nodules develop on the roots of some species. For convenience, the fibrous-rooted species are grouped according to similarity in flowers, leaves, or stems under two divisions, depending on whether the spur (mentioned on page 17) is short or long. Among the short-spurred species immediately following are some of the parental types of *P. domesticum*. Long-spurred species, commencing on page 128, include, among others, the progenitors of *P. hortorum*.

Short-Spurred Pelargoniums

A variety of habit and leaf-shape is found among the short-spurred species. A number of them have short, thick, succulent stems that are often gnarled in appearance. Here are such species as *P. cotyledonis* with white flowers and rounded or heart-shaped, wrinkled leaves, *P. paradoxum* with spoon-shaped to partially pinnate leaves on the same plant, *P. alternans*, *P. carnosum*, *P. crithmifolium* and *P. dasycaule* with pinnately divided leaves. Others are shrubby in habit with slender stems and palmately nerved or lobed leaves. Large and brightly colored flowers abound in this group, which includes *P. angulosum*, *P. betulinum*, *P. cordifolium*, *P. cucullatum*, *P. hispidum* and *P. papilionaceum*.

Low, Thick-Stemmed Species

P. alternans Wendl.—Stems thick, succulent with short erect branches, the whole plant up to one foot or so high; leaves small, to three inches long, hairy, pinnately divided into three-lobed, fan-shaped segments suggesting pinnules of the maidenhair fern in size and shape; umbels one or a few on each branch, two- to four-flowered, the nearly sessile white flowers marked with red on the upper petals, spur about as long as the sepals, upper petals narrow and not as noticeably uneven at the base as in *P. carnosum* and other species. Introduced to England from South Africa about 1791. Illustrated by Sweet, t. 286, as *Otidia alternans*.

P. carnosum (L.) L'Hér. ex Ait.—Main stems thick, fleshy-woody, gnarled, to six inches long with few short branches, plants in flower reaching a foot or more; leaves smooth or minutely hairy, fleshy, to four inches long, ovate-oblong in general outline and pinnately lobed to or nearly to the midrib, the lobes irregularly wedge-shaped with incised and toothed margins; inflorescence usually of several six- to eight-flowered umbels on long peduncles, the flowers white or pale pink on bristly pedicels up to three-fourths inch long, the spur generally shorter than the sepals. Introduced into England from South Africa before 1724 and occasionally cultivated in the United States. Illustrated by Sweet, t. 98, as *Otidia carnosa*.

P. cotyledonis (L.) L'Hér. ex Ait.—Stems short, thick, fleshy-woody; leaves deciduous, to two inches or more, ovate, heart-shaped at base with the lobes more or less overlapping so that the leaf sometimes appears peltate, obscurely lobed and toothed along the margin, densely white-hairy below when young, yellow green, rugose (puckered in appearance) above; inflorescence a short panicle of several-flowered umbels, the pediceled white flowers with an extremely short spur and nearly equal white petals giving more the appearance of a flower in the genus *Geranium*. Brought to England from St. Helena in 1765. Illustrated by L'Héritier, t. 27 and as *Geranium cotyledonis* by Andrews, *Geraniums* vol. 2, t. 75. Observed at the New York Botanical Garden and grown by the author several years ago.

P. crithmifolium Smith—Stems thick, woody-fleshy, with herbaceous branches swollen at the nodes, the whole plant up to two feet tall or more; leaves succulent, to a little over three inches long, glaucous-green, clustered at ends of branches, pinnately lobed, the segments again pinnate, deeply toothed or incised; inflorescence branched with numerous three- to ten-flowered umbels, the large, showy, white flowers on slender pedicels, the spur shorter than the sepals, petals all spotted with red, the upper slightly longer than the lower and with larger spots. Native in southwest Cape Province, South Africa. Cultivated in England before 1790. Illustrated by Sweet, t. 354, as *Otidia crithmifolia*. Deciduous.

P. *dasycaule* Haw.—Similar to P. *crithmifolium* but with leaves less divided, the lobes oblong or ovate in outline and mostly bluntly three-toothed at the tip. Grown in England before 1812 but not definitely known in the wild state. Illustrated in *Curtis's Botanical Magazine* t. 2029 (1819). Deciduous.

P. *paradoxum* Dinter—Stems thick, fleshy-woody, gnarled, erect, little-branched, to a little more than two feet high, the branches short and stubby; leaves fleshy, four inches long or slightly more, over an inch broad, spoon-shaped, the margins rather wavy-crisped and crenately lobed, bristly-hairy; inflorescence terminal, composed of three to five umbels bearing four or five or occasionally up to ten white flowers with short spurs and nearly equal petals. Discovered in Namaqualand, South Africa, 1922. Plants under cultivation often have more than one kind of leaf, some of them being deeply divided in various ways although the species was originally described with entire leaves.

TALL, SLENDER-STEMMED, SHRUBBY SPECIES

P. *angulosum* (Mill.) L'Hér. ex Ait.—Shrubby; stems harshly hairy, branched, woody, up to three feet tall or more; leaves short-petioled, to two inches long or more, rigid, strongly ribbed, wedge-shaped at the base, sharply and shallowly three- to five-lobed or -angled, resembling the contour of common mallow or hibiscus leaves, softly hairy to nearly smooth, the margins coarsely toothed; umbels axillary or several in a short panicle, short-stalked, with three to seven nearly sessile, short-spurred, violet-rose flowers about an inch long. Known to Dillenius and cultivated in England before 1724. Large patches of these plants grow wild at the base of Twelve Apostle Mountains near Capetown, South Africa, and present a vividly colorful picture when in bloom. P. *angulosum* is one of the principal parent species of P. *domesticum*. The name of a related species, P. *acerifolium*, having more deeply lobed leaves, is sometimes found in catalogs. Plants listed by that name have been found to be misnamed.

P. *betulinum* (L.) L'Hér. ex Ait.—Shrubby; stems slender,

branched, erect, to three feet or more; leaves small, to a little more
than one-half inch long, rounded and sharply toothed at the apex,
wedge-shaped to truncate at the base, smooth or nearly so; umbels
numerous at the tips of branches, two- to four-flowered, the lavender-
pink flowers with a spur nearly as long as the sepals, the upper petals
dark-veined, an inch or more long. A South African species introduced
into England about 1786. Not now in cultivation but one of the
species involved in the production of *P. domesticum.*

P. cordifolium (Cav.) Curt. (syn. *P. cordatum* Ait.)—Shrubby;
stems to three feet or more, branched; leaves long-petioled with heart-
shaped blades somewhat resembling those of a lilac in size and shape,
glossy and slightly hairy above, densely white-hairy below, the margins
finely toothed; inflorescence an axillary panicle of four- to seven-flowered umbels, the pale to bright pink flowers with a spur about as long
as the sepals, the upper petals feathered purple, broader and more
deeply colored than the very slender lower ones. Introduced into
England from South Africa in 1774. Illustrated in *Curtis's Botanical
Magazine* t. 165 (1792) and by Sweet, t. 67.

P. cucullatum (L.) L'Hér. ex Ait.—Shrubby; stems to four feet or
more, branched, woody, densely soft hairy; leaves to four inches or
more on long petioles, reniform, cordate at the base, somewhat
cupped, the margins finely toothed and sometimes obscurely lobed;
inflorescence an axillary panicle of five- to ten-flowered umbels, the
showy crimson-purple flowers with a spur shorter than the sepals and
with petals to an inch or more long, the upper two feathered with
purple. Introduced into England in 1690. Wild plants are cultivated
in Capetown gardens. *P. cucullatum* is one of the principal species
involved in *P. domesticum.*

P. hispidum (L. f.) Willd.—A large shrub, vigorous, woody, erect,
to four feet tall or more, branched and glandular-hairy; leaves large,
long-petioled, to six inches, palmately lobed, the lobes pointed and
furnished with secondary pointed lobelets, the margins incised,
coarsely toothed and ciliate; inflorescence branched with four- to
eight-flowered umbels, the flowers pink, the spur shorter than the
sepals, the upper petals brighter than the lower ones and purple-
veined at base. Habitat moist, shady, alpine situations in eastern Cape
Colony, South Africa. Introduced into England before 1800.

P. papilionaceum (L.) L'Hér. ex Ait.—Stems hairy, woody at the
base, herbaceous above old growth, much branched, to about three

feet high; leaves long-petioled, hairy, orbicular in outline, heart-shaped at the base, bluntly five- to seven-lobed, the lobes shallow and toothed; umbels panicled, five- to ten-flowered, the small flowers with a spur shorter than the sepals and the pink upper petals spotted with purple, much longer than the white lower petals, which scarcely equal the sepals in length. Native in South Africa, growing in moist, shaded places; cultivated in Chelsea Garden, England, 1724. Illustrated by Sweet, t. 27.

Long-Spurred Pelargoniums

Some of the most brilliant and bizarre of all are included in the long-spurred group. *Pelargonium tetragonum* and *P. endlicherianum* have two very conspicuous upper petals and extremely small, pale lower petals. Each is unusual for another reason, *P. tetragonum* being the only species with angled stems, *P. endlicherianum* being one of the few species growing naturally outside continental Africa and the only one known to be hardy in northern climates. All the rest have lower petals that are noticeable and at least half as long as the upper petals.

Three species and one hybrid—*P. echinatum* and its derivative, *P. stapletonii*, both bearing spines, along with *P. crassicaule* and *P. reniforme*—have thickish stems and leaves that are densely white-hairy on the underside. The remainder being treated here have green leaves. In one group of species the leaves are deeply five- to seven-lobed with sharp teeth on the margins. Here are found *P. alchemilloides*, *P. grandiflorum*, the problematical plants called *P. palmatum*, yellow-flowered *P. praemorsum*, and an interesting new clone from Japan, *Pelargonium* 'Fingered Flowers.'

In the last group the resemblance to *P. hortorum* is easily seen, for all these species have green leaves with very shallow lobes or none, also scalloped margins with rounded teeth. *Pelargonium inquinans* and *P. zonale* are already familiar as the main parents of the garden geranium. Similar to these are *P. acetosum*, *P. burtoniae*, *P. frutetorum*, *P. salmoneum* and *P. scandens*.

Species with Very Short Lower Petals

P. endlicherianum Fenzl—Herbaceous perennial with erect, leafy, simple or branched flowering stem from a basal rosette of cordate-orbicular or reniform, crenately toothed and shallowly five-lobed, softly hairy leaves to three inches broad; flowering stem to three feet high or more with one or more long-stalked umbels of five to fifteen rose-pink, dark-veined, sweetly scented, nearly sessile flowers, the spur twice as long as the sepals or more, the two upper petals broadly obovate and clawed, much longer than the three lower petals, which are shorter than the recurved sepals. Native in Asia Minor and the only hardy pelargonium in cultivation. Illustrated in *Curtis's Botanical Magazine*, t. 4946 (1856).

P. *tetragonum* (L.f.) L'Hér. ex Ait.—Stems to about three feet high, green, fleshy, square or triangular, jointed, smooth, few-leaved; leaves to an inch long or slightly more, reniform or cordate, shallowly five-lobed with crenately toothed margins or the upper leaves somewhat three-lobed, long-hairy; umbels axillary with one to three (often two) sessile flowers having a spur more than twice as long as the sepals, and usually four petals, the two upper petals bent backward, long-clawed, purplish rose with dark veins, and much longer than the very short, slender white or pale pink lower petals. A South African species introduced into England by Masson, 1774. Illustrated by Sweet, t. 99, as *Jenkinsonia tetragona*. Deciduous.

SPECIES WITH WHITE-HAIRY UNDERSURFACES ON LEAVES

P. *crassicaule* L'Hér. ex Ait.—Stems to a foot tall or more, thick, fleshy-woody, armed with spines; leaves small, about an inch wide and slightly longer, rather fan-shaped, tapering narrowly into the petiole, the rounded apex incised and coarsely toothed; five- to nine-flowered umbels several on flowering branches, the white flowers with spur several times as long as the sepals, all or only the two upper petals spotted with red. Reported to grow five feet tall in South Africa. Introduced into England about 1785. Illustrated by Sweet, t. 192.

P. *echinatum* Curt.—Stem thick, fleshy, armed with persistent spinelike stipules, little-branched; long-petioled leaves arise in clusters from the ends of stems and are smaller on the branches, the blades to four inches long, thin, light green above, softly and densely white-hairy below, cordate-ovate in outline, shallowly three- to seven-lobed, the margins toothed; umbels often several, many-flowered, the white to purple, nearly sessile flowers crimson-spotted on the upper petals, the spur several times as long as the sepals. Native in South Africa. Introduced into England in 1795 by Masson. Illustrated in *Curtis's*

Botanical Magazine t. 309 (1795) and by Sweet, t. 54. Sometimes clusters of both white and purple occur on the same plant. Deciduous.

P. reniforme Curt.—Stems low, thick, fleshy, with slender flowering branches; leaves round or kidney-shaped with toothed margins, to one and one-half inches long, green and minutely hairy above, densely and softly white-hairy below; umbels usually several and panicled, five- to twenty-flowered, the smallish flowers with a spur several times as long as the sepals, and with bright magenta petals, the upper two blackish spotted in the center. Native in South Africa. Introduced into England about 1798. Illustrated in *Curtis's Botanical Magazine* t. 493 (1800) and by Sweet, t. 48.

P. × stapletonii Sweet.—A hybrid of *P. echinatum* crossed with the progeny of *P. echinatum* × *P. reniforme*; similar to *P. echinatum* from which it differs in having leaves that are usually slightly smaller, more softly white-hairy when young, and not as deeply nor as uniformly lobed; magenta-purple flowers are spotted with deeper color in the center of each petal. Developed in England before 1820. Illustrated by Sweet, t. 212. Deciduous.

Species with Deeply Lobed, Sharply Toothed, Green Leaves

P. alchemilloides (L.) L'Hér. ex. Ait.—Herbaceous perennial, many-stemmed; leaves long-petioled, about one and one-half inches long, reniform in outline and five- to seven-lobed to the middle or deeper, the margins sharply toothed, softly pubescent and marked with a dark zone toward the base; umbels long-stalked with three to six small flowers, the spur twice as long as the sepals or more, the petals white, marked rose-pink on the upper two. South African species introduced into England about 1693.

'Fingered Flowers'—Stems succulent-woody, erect, rather thick and somewhat like those of *P. zonale* derivatives, about one foot tall, branched, the branches short; leaves kidney-shaped or almost like those of the maidenhair tree (*Ginkgo*) in outline, small, to two inches or more, palmately and deeply three- to five-lobed, lobes coarsely toothed at outer edge of leaf, bright green with dark purplish zone; inflorescence extending beyond the foliage with several flowers in the cluster, each flower more than an inch across, five- to nine-petaled, soft-salmon, the petals linear, about one-eighth inch wide.

Called "Fingered Flowers" in Japan, a plant was first brought to Mexico in 1947 by a naval officer and was introduced from there by

Mr. M. H. Arndt. The name translated from the Japanese is formally adopted here. Of apparent hybrid origin, this is a distinctive pelargonium with flowers that suggest a rayed daisy. Plants are deciduous, shedding their leaves during the winter months.

P. *grandiflorum* Willd.—Shrubby, stems woody, erect, to two feet high or more and usually single; leaves long-petioled, two to three inches broad, smooth, glaucous, deeply five-lobed and sharply toothed along the margins; umbels axillary with two to three large white flowers red-veined on the upper petals, the spur about three times as long as the sepals, upper petals broader than the lower. Native in South Africa. Introduced into England about 1794. Illustrated by Sweet, t. 29. This species was one of the early parents of P. *domesticum* but its effect is scarcely visible now.

P. *multibracteatum* Hochst.—Stems herbaceous or woody at the base, to two feet or more high, erect or bent over at the base, branching; leaves bright green, not zoned, round or kidney-shaped in outline, heart-shaped at the base, the lower ones to four inches or more across, the upper smaller, all deeply five- to seven-lobed beyond the middle of the blade, sharply toothed along the margins, slightly hairy when young; umbels axillary, long-stalked, three- to twelve-flowered, the spur several times as long as the sepals, the white, nearly equal petals tinged with pink toward the base. Native in moist, shady places in tropical Africa. Observed at Kew Gardens but not cultivated in America. Illustrated in *Flowering Plants of South Africa* t. 794 (1940).

P. *palmatum*—An obscure name which cannot be definitely verified as literature has not revealed a description. Although there is a plant that has been cultivated under the name P. *palmatum*, it has not been seen in bloom by me nor by pelargonium fanciers with whom I am acquainted, and until it flowers it cannot be accurately determined. Because it is distinctive, the following partial description is given here:—herbaceous perennial; stems erect, to about a foot high, few-branched; leaves thin, on long petioles, kidney-shaped in outline, about three inches wide, five- to seven-lobed, the lobes wedge-shaped and cut to one-third the depth of the blade, silky hairy above, the margins crenately toothed and ciliate, smaller leaves at base of plant sometimes zoned.

P. *praemorsum* (Andr.) Dietr. [P. *quinatum* Sims]—Stems woody, slender, lax, shining brown, branching; petioles short to long, leaves to an inch, orbicular or reniform, deeply five-lobed, the lobes wedge-shaped, thin, toothed at the ends, sometimes zoned; umbels of one or usually two creamy-buff flowers, the spur about twice as long as the sepals, petals four or five, the upper purple-veined, more than twice as long as the lower, which are only slightly longer than the sepals. Introduced into England from South Africa about 1798. Illustrated by Sweet, t. 79, as *Jenkinsonia quinata.*

SPECIES WITH SHALLOWLY LOBED, ROUND-TOOTHED, GREEN LEAVES

P. acetosum (L.) L'Hér. ex Ait.—Shrubby; stems succulent, slender and lax; leaves on short petioles, the somewhat fleshy, smooth, glaucous blades about one inch long, obovate in outline with wedge-shaped base and rounded, shallowly lobed and toothed apex; umbels axillary, two- to seven-flowered, the spur two to three or more times as long as the sepals, the very slender, almost equal petals blush pink to pink. South African species cultivated in England before 1724. Illustrated in *Curtis's Botanical Magazine* t. 103 (1789).

P. burtoniae L. Bolus—Shrubby; stems succulent and branched or sometimes scrambling; leaves to one and one-half inches long, yellow green, slightly fleshy, nearly glabrous, reniform or orbicular with cordate or truncate base and irregularly toothed margin; umbels axillary with many bright coral-red, nearly sessile flowers having a spur about three times as long as the sepals, the upper petals erect with recurved tips, the lower bent downward. Discovered in South Africa about 1924.

P. frutetorum R. A. Dyer—Shrubby; stems slender, branched and lax, sometimes scrambling; leaves to two inches or more long, bright green with a wide dark zone, more or less orbicular with cordate base, thin, sparsely soft-hairy, shallowly five-lobed, the lobes with rounded teeth; umbels axillary, hairy, extending well beyond the leaves, with many large salmon-pink, nearly sessile flowers, the spur several times as long as the sepals, the petals obovate, rather broad and nearly equal. Discovered in eastern Cape Province, South Africa, 1931. Illustrated in *Hooker's Icones Plantarum*, t. 3200 (1933). At Kew Gardens and in the United States, variations of this species occur. In both cases the leaves are black green with wide green margins. The flowers of the English variety are scarlet; those of the American variety are orange salmon and are distributed commercially under the name of 'Black Beauty.'

P. inquinans (L.) L'Hér. ex Ait.—Shrubby; stems softly woody, branched, to six feet high; leaves orbicular, deeply cordate at the base and shallowly five- to seven-lobed with toothed lobes, to three inches wide, softly hairy and lacking a dark zone; umbels axillary with many nearly sessile scarlet or less often pink to white flowers having a glandular-hairy spur two or more times as long as the sepals, the petals bluntly obovate, the two upper slightly shorter than the lower. Native in South Africa but now naturalized in many parts of the world. Introduced into England by 1714. Illustrated in *Flowering Plants of South Africa* t. 981 (1946).

P. salmoneum R. A. Dyer—Similar to *P. zonale* with stems to nearly three feet high but the leaves scarcely or not at all zoned, more or less glaucous, fleshy and softly hairy and the fewer flowers salmon-pink nerved with red on the upper petals. Found under cultivation in Port Elizabeth, South Africa, about 1930. Illustrated in *Curtis's Botanical Magazine* t. 9357 (1934) and in *Flowering Plants of South Africa* t. 971 (1946).

P. scandens Ehrh.—Shrubby; stems slender, lax, flexuous, ascending to two feet or more, little branched; leaves glossy green, smooth, rounded in outline with bluntish to slightly wedge-shaped base and crenately toothed margins; umbels axillary or opposite the leaves, three- to twelve-flowered, the pale rose-white flowers with a spur twice as long as the sepals or more, the upper petals dark veined. Described from plants cultivated at the Berlin Botanical Garden about 1790 and later found native in South Africa. Plants by this name presently under cultivation differ from the original in having leaves more like *P. hortorum* at the base and are probably incorrectly named.

P. zonale (L.) L'Hér. ex Ait.—Shrubby; stems softly woody, branched, softly hairy when young, to three feet or more high; leaves to three inches broad or more, orbicular, cordate at the base and crenately toothed along the margin, minutely bristly hairy, bright green with a dark zone shaped like a horseshoe; umbels axillary, eight inches tall or more with many pink or less frequently red, nearly sessile flowers having a more or less smooth spur two or more times as long as the sepals, and narrow, obovate or strap-shaped, nearly equal petals. Introduced into England from South Africa in 1710. Large specimens five feet high are naturalized on rocky hillsides near Lisbon, Portugal.

PART III

Culture

Chapter 1

BASIC NEEDS

In most regions, to grow geraniums outdoors means bringing them in or protecting them as soon as the cold approaches. The roots of none are hardy during prolonged winter weather except one known species, *Pelargonium endlicherianum*.

Where the thermometer seldom drops below freezing the year around, plants may be quite safely left in the ground. In "exceptional" weather, however, protection of branches and roots from frost may be required for a time. In such a climate the pelargoniums merely slacken their growth during spells of low temperature. Over the course of a year they will reach great size.

On the other hand, where summers are short and winters impose many months of indoor culture, smaller stature is the rule. Thus behavior varies in different climatic situations. The principles of culture, however, are the same wherever pelargoniums are grown.

One reason why these plants have been popular for many generations is undoubtedly that most of them endure a wide range of growing conditions. Members of the *P. hortorum* group (the garden geranium), also the ivy-leaved and scented-leaved kinds, are easily handled either outdoors or under cover.

Merely to endure a diversity of situations is, however, far different from the state of vigorous growth attainable when ideal surroundings are provided. A thorough understanding of the plants' basic needs will bring its reward in the form of finer growth.

137

SOILS AND THEIR ADJUNCTS

Pelargoniums will grow in sandy or clay soil, but they will repay the grower if a little attention is given in preparing a friable and nourishing one. Sandy soil retains neither water nor nourishment. Therefore, humus is needed to improve its texture and water holding capacity. Clay soils are sticky. They pack, bake and become water logged so that the clods must be broken up by mixing it with humus material and coarse sand. Nutrients in the soil are also necessary to encourage good growth and the production of flowers.

The proper basis for the soil mixture for Pelargoniums is a garden loam that is fairly heavy and friable. Added to this, to improve the texture and furnish extra nutrients, there should be some humus, some sharp coarse sand, and some ground limestone. A small amount of superphosphate is added by some commercial growers. Too rich a soil or too much nitrogen will produce excessive leaf growth at the expense of flowers.

The soil mixture should be of such a consistency that if squeezed in the hand it falls apart when the pressure is released. If too wet or clayey, it fails to do this and will cling together. On the other hand, if too dry or sandy it refuses to bind at all. The soil should be porous so that it permits free drainage of water, and at the same time the humus content should be such as to insure the retention of moisture about the roots. A neutral or mildly acid soil with a pH between 6.5 and 8 is considered satisfactory for growing pelargoniums.

Humus

A compost pile or pit as a source of humus is of inestimable value to every gardener. Humus is the product of organic material that has become dark brown and crumbly from being thoroughly decomposed. To build a compost pile it is best to start at the bottom with inverted sod or other coarse material, and then add alternate layers of soil and vegetable matter such as leaves, weeds, grass clippings, garden and kitchen waste, hay, straw or other litter. The pile should be wider at the bottom than at the top, and the top should be slightly concave or depressed in order to catch as much rain water as possible. Decomposition of this organic material is hastened by sprinkling commercial fertilizer over each layer of vegetable matter. The resulting product is of particular value for potted plants grown in the house or greenhouse; it is also useful in lightening the texture of the soil of flower beds in gardens.

The gardener's needs for humus may be amply supplied from the compost pile, but the commercial grower often finds it necessary to increase the bulk by adding peatmoss. In the West, peatmoss is extensively used also by home gardeners.

Infected plants or soil which has previously been used for them should not be added to the pile. If infected material has already been placed on the pile, the humus should be sterilized. A simple method for the gardener is to fill a bread pan with humus and then place it in an oven heated to 350 degrees and maintain that temperature for thirty minutes. If larger quantities of humus in larger pans are to be sterilized the baking time should be increased. In commercial greenhouses sterilization is accomplished by using live steam. Greenhouses where only sterilized soil is used have little trouble with pests and diseases.

Leafmold is another excellent source of humus; it is the result of leaves, twigs, and fallen bits of bark of deciduous trees slowly decomposing on the ground. If this material is coarse it should be rubbed through a quarter-inch mesh screen to break it up into smaller particles.

Commercial growers of many thousands of garden geraniums each year sometimes grow their own "green" humus by planting a field with rye seed, and ploughing it under when it has grown to about six inches. By the end of a year it is mellow enough to use in potting mixtures. The rotted blades of grass and roots supply a fibrous quality of humus.

Peatmoss is sometimes substituted for leafmold or compost to lighten the soil. This material, however, tends to pack firmly. It is necessary to exercise good judgment in proportioning the ingredients of the soil mixture to make sure that it is of an open and friable consistency.

Soil from abandoned mushroom beds is used to a great extent where mushroom culture is carried on. Since this is basically horse manure, it still contains abundant humus as well as nutrients after it has served its original purpose. Mushroom soil should be unadulterated with clay if it is used as humus in composing a soil for potted plants.

Sand

Sharp coarse sand should be clean if used for plants. If it is not clean it is a simple matter to cleanse it by pouring water through it and allowing it to drain off before mixing it with loam and humus. Fine sand should not be used as it packs so firmly that it prevents the free passage of water.

Fertilizer

The nutrients that plants require are obtained in solution from the soil by absorption through the roots. Organic fertilizer provides most of the necessary minerals. However, this is sometimes supplemented with commercial fertilizer depending upon the experience of the grower and the condition of the plant.

Organic fertilizer such as stable manure is an excellent source of nourishment for plants. It is preferable that straw or litter be mixed with it, to give it a fibrous quality, and together they should be so thoroughly decomposed that the mixture is dark and crumbly. If this has been added to the compost pile, no other fertilizer need be added to the potting mixture. However, some of our best commercial growers add a small amount of superphosphate, and some finely ground limestone to keep the soil near the neutral pH level.

If the initial soil has been adequately supplied with nutrients, plants do not need to be fed unless they become potbound. Good commercial fertilizers are available, but in the experience of many successful growers, a formula should contain little or no nitrogen and about equal amounts of potash and phosphate. A formula of 0-10-10 or 2-10-10 (the figures are on the package) may be used dry or in liquid form. In regions where the natural soil is low in nitrogen, however, this element must be supplied. Field-grown stock in California, for example, seems to require added nitrogen more than plants grown in the East.

Since there are different kinds of humus and fertilizers which can be added to garden loam and sand, a few formulas have been prepared to suit the gardener's needs or convenience.

FORMULA 1—8 parts garden loam, 3 parts humus, 3 parts sharp coarse sand, 2 parts well rotted manure. To each bushel of mixture add a three-inch flower-potful of finely ground limestone.

FORMULA 2—1 part heavy garden loam, 1 part sharp coarse sand, 1 part humus to which rotted manure was added in the original preparation of the compost pile, plus a three-inch flower-potful of finely ground limestone. To this soil composition Mr. M. H. Arndt, hybridist and grower of specimen plants, adds a three-inch potful of superphosphate. Moreover, he uses this fertilized mixture for growing mature pelargoniums of all classes as well as raising them from seeds or cuttings. My experience with this soil in growing all kinds of pelargoniums proved most satisfactory.

FORMULA 3—3 parts heavy garden loam, 1 part well rotted manure. To each one and a half bushels of this add a four-inch potful of complete fertilizer such as 4-12-4. This formula is recommended by Mr. R. M. Henley, *P. domesticum* specialist of Indiana, for mature plants of this group.

When setting the plants in the open ground for year-round growth, the flower bed should be prepared to a depth of ten to twelve inches with a sandy loam to which some stable manure has been added. Additional fertilizer should not be applied more than once a year. Pot-grown plants, with only a limited amount of soil available to their roots, require a slightly richer mixture. Because of the drier atmosphere in an inhabited room, an even heavier, more retentive soil is required there than in a greenhouse where a moister atmosphere prevails.

Although pelargoniums of the four major groups will grow in any reasonably good soil, a little care will produce more luxuriant plants and larger flowers.

A fifth group, the tuberous-rooted pelargoniums, which shed their leaves, require a loose soil mixture such as indicated in formula 2. For further directions on their culture see the section on watering (page 143).

AIR, WATER, AND ADDED NUTRIENTS

Surroundings which will induce healthy growth supplement good choice of soil in keeping plants in prime condition. Particularly indoors, where atmosphere and moisture can be regulated, attention needs to be given to the temperature, the flow of air, and to the watering and feeding of the plants.

Temperature

Except for a few species native in tropical Africa, (of which *P. multibracteatum* is probably the only one in cultivation) most pelargoniums will tolerate a wide range of temperature. But there is a definite range which is desirable for their maximum development. A temperature of 55 to 65 degrees at night, and 70 degrees during the day is considered ideal. Higher temperatures due to sunheat at midday are beneficial during the growing season.

Pelargonium domesticum varieties must have cool night air not reaching over 60 degrees for flower buds to form. At higher temperatures these plants vegetate more rapidly. Flowers do not appear until three months after the temperature has been reduced.

Light

Low light intensity during short days of midwinter in the colder parts of America also reduces and sometimes prevents flowering. As the days lengthen and the sun becomes stronger bud formation is encouraged.

In any season, pelargoniums require full sunlight for at least a part of the day, and preferably all day. They will not grow or flower satisfactorily in full shade. As a general rule it will be found that pale or delicately colored flowers will retain their color better if the plants are protected against intense afternoon sunshine.

Similarly, if pelargoniums are grown in a window, a southern or southeastern exposure is best suited to them. If plants are kept in one position for any length of time the leaves all turn toward the light and they become unevenly balanced. In order to avoid this tendency the pots should be turned occasionally so that all parts of the plant may receive an equal amount of light. In this way the growth will develop more symmetrically.

Ventilation

Pelargoniums grown in the house or greenhouse need an ample supply of fresh circulating air. Even in cold weather it is advisable to open a window for a few minutes each day.

Whether grown indoors or outdoors plants should not be crowded together for any length of time. There should be enough space between them so that air can circulate around each plant. The amount of space necessary depends upon the type and variety of the plants grown. When they are bedded out, the garden geraniums should be spaced at least a foot apart; *P. crispum* requires less space; *P. denticulatum* needs two feet or even more.

In addition to freely moving air, most pelargoniums prefer an atmosphere that is not too moist. These conditions will prevent the leaves and stems from becoming soft, and will also minimize the danger of fungus and bacterial action.

Watering

The environment in which pelargoniums are grown determines the necessity and frequency of watering, and the method of watering varies also according to circumstances. On dull days or in cold weather leaves give off less moisture; therefore, the roots need less water. Conversely, when the weather is sunny and warm, more moisture is given off by the leaves so that the roots require more water. As plants give off moisture through their leaves it becomes essential for them to absorb more liquid through their roots.

Pelargoniums grown in the house may need watering every day or every other day during the summer. Those grown in greenhouses where a moister atmosphere usually prevails, also those grown in the ground, may need watering two or three times a week. No general rule can be made. Under some circumstances, for example, a pot-bound plant with ample foliage in a light and somewhat airy position may require watering more than once a day. Moreover, large plants in small pots will need attention more often than will plants of moderate size in large pots. Plants in ten- to fourteen-inch pots or tubs may need to be watered thoroughly only once a week. The sides of most containers are exposed to sun and air and have drying effect on the soil in which they are growing. Plants grown in the open ground benefit from rainfall, but during dry spells thorough watering before the soil becomes too dry is essential.

During the winter months, when less evaporation takes place, pelargoniums grown indoors require less watering than in summer. Plants growing in a heavy soil mixture require less frequent watering than those growing in a more sandy medium. Plants that are in full flower and in active growth require liberal quantities of water. Allowing the soil to remain dry during the active growing period reduces growth and delays flowering, and often causes reddening of the leaves followed by leaf-drying.

On the other hand, it should be stressed that overwatering is as serious a fault as underwatering. The soil should be kept moist at all times during the growing period but not soaking wet.

Watering should be done only when necessary, and then the entire ball of earth in the pot should be thoroughly saturated, and any surplus water should be allowed to drain off. A potted pelargonium should not stand in a saucer of water for any length of time as this prevents air from entering the soil and the result will be a sickly plant. The surface of the soil should feel dry to the touch before water is applied again.

During their resting period pelargoniums that retain their leaves and stems should not lack for water, but it should be given more sparingly than when growth is active. Pelargoniums that lose their leaves when resting, such as *P. gibbosum, P. tetragonum* and *P. crithmifolium,* are kept quite dry until growth is about to be resumed.

The best time for watering is in the morning before the plants have been heated by the sun. The alternative is watering in the late afternoon if the leaves can be kept from getting wet. When drops of water stand on leaves overnight, mildew is likely to set in.

Pelargoniums grown in a house where the atmosphere is dry benefit by occasional syringing during the summer months. There are several advantages to be derived from syringing: (1) It increases the humidity of the surrounding atmosphere, and reduces the evaporation power of the air. (2) It helps in keeping the leaves of the plants free of the dust and dirt which shuts the sunshine, air, and moisture from their surfaces. Syringing should be done early in the day in bright, sunny weather.

During their resting period in winter, when new growth seems temporarily to cease, pelargoniums that retain their leaves should not lack for moisture at their roots. Water, however, should be given more sparingly than when growth is active.

There are pelargoniums within the genus that differ from all others in that they shed their leaves or leaves and stems, and then enter a resting period for three months or longer before starting into growth again. Among these deciduous plants are tuberous-rooted pelargoniums such as *P. rapaceum* and *P. ardens*; plants with stems that are swollen at the joints as in *P. gibbosum* and *P. crithmifolium*; angular as in *P. tetragonum*; and thick, fleshy-stemmed kinds such as *P. apiifolium* and *P. echinatum*.

These deciduous plants prefer a droughtlike condition when they are dormant. This was well demonstrated by Mr. Arndt of Hightstown, N. J., to garden club members and other visitors who returned to his greenhouse periodically during one year to observe a plant he had chosen for an extreme experiment. He pulled a fleshy, bare-stemmed pelargonium out of a flower pot and placed it on a table in the greenhouse where it lay for more than three months with the roots exposed. During that time, no water was applied to it. When leaf-buds appeared the plant was potted in a rich soil mixture (see page 141), and normal watering was begun. The plant responded favorably to this seemingly drastic treatment in that it grew vigorously and produced an abundance of healthy foliage as well as flowers of good quality.

It is not actually recommended that deciduous pelargoniums should be taken out of their containers when they have reached their dormant phase. It is, however, extremely important to keep plants of this type quite dry while they are resting. Only when they begin to show signs of growth should normal watering be resumed. At the same time they should be given a light and airy position so that they can grow and spread in a natural manner.

Feeding

Feeding of potted plants should only be attempted when they have pretty well filled their containers with healthy roots. Geraniums do best in a soil relatively high in phosphorus and potash and low in nitrogen yet not so low that disease resistance is impaired. Phosphorus stimulates root and plant growth, and potash brings out the flower colors.

The best proportioned chemical fertilizer for them contains nitrogen, phosphorus and potash in the proportion of 0-10-10, 2-10-10 or 5-10-10, depending on the soil to which it is added A generous pinch (one-fourth teaspoonful) of any one of these to a four-inch pot should be scratched into the surface of the soil about every four or five weeks, before the soil has become dry, and then it should be watered in thoroughly. If the soil mixture in which the pelargoniums are grown is of loose texture it is preferable to use fertilizer in solution, as the humus in the soil mixture acts as a reservoir and aids in releasing the chemical elements necessary for good growth. Weak solutions of chemical fertilizers may be used at more frequent intervals than stronger solutions. Liquid fertilizer should be applied in place of water, and it is advisable to use the solutions before the soil in the pot has become too dry.

This regular feeding nourishes potbound plants which have utilized most of the fertilizers originally contained in the soil mixture, and aids in preventing the lower leaves from dropping. Plants whose roots are crowded in small containers should be fed more frequently than those in larger containers. A weaker solution applied about every two weeks will keep them in good condition.

Contrary to the practice of some of the eastern growers, westerners have recently been feeding larger proportions of nitrogen to their geranium plots. One of the claims is that it makes for firm branches with short nodes, which they look upon as a double advantage when propagating from cuttings.

Chapter 2

PROPAGATION

Every geranium plant in one's possession is a potential parent of numerous offspring. New plants in quantity may be obtained either from cuttings or seeds.

INCREASE FROM STEM CUTTINGS

The quickest way to increase one's stock of geraniums is to grow them from cuttings, or slips, taken from healthy plants on hand. Most of them will root readily in two to three weeks, though some take several months. To shorten the time and also to increase the production of roots on cuttings, a rooting hormone may be used. Directions on the container should be explicitly followed.

Pelargonium hortorum and *P. peltatum* varieties often flower quite soon after rooting. *P. domesticum* varieties generally seem to be slower to bloom, because they take longer to root. Their flowering is dependent on the time of year rather than on the time elapsed after rooting; consequently it may be either further retarded or advanced in relation to the season.

The new plants derived from cuttings will in time look exactly like the old. For example, a gardener propagating *Pelargonium scarboroviae* will be able to obtain a specimen essentially identical with the first plant of this kind to be observed in an English greenhouse a century ago. The characteristics of the original have been duplicated

147

through each succeeding generation of plants by vegetative means. It is only by using an actual piece (not a seed) from the parent that the new plant can be assured of resembling the original. In the same way new varieties arising today can be perpetuated for tomorrow's gardens.

Sometimes a new form may be a bud mutation, or sport. This is a single branch which, for no reason easily explainable, assumes a character different from the rest of the plant. If the new traits are desirable—as they often are—they may be perpetuated vegetatively.

A pelargonium cutting may be taken either from the stem or from a branch. Those made from the tip are preferable to the woodier sections lower down for they root more readily. It is important that they be cut from regions of recent but mature growth on clean, sturdy specimens. Old stems or branches are too woody to favor root formation, and new growth is so soft and sappy that it is apt to rot. Cuttings should be sliced cleanly across with a clean, sharp knife just below a node or joint, and take no leaves or parts of leaves from them. Since leggy cuttings develop into spindly plants, short-jointed sections are preferable. Cuttings should not be allowed to wilt; they are best planted as soon as they are taken.

Two- to four-inch cuttings may be planted directly in two-and-a-quarter-inch-pots. Six-inch or even longer cuttings of garden geraniums or large scented-leaved kinds are planted in four-inch pots in which they root and grow and come into flower. The garden geranium raised from long cuttings in four-inch pots will flower in about eleven or twelve weeks from the time the cuttings are planted.

If the growing medium was not sterilized, the base of a cutting may be moistened and dipped in a disinfectant such as permalite immediately before planting it.

Before potting up cuttings the soil should be watered and allowed to drain. A space below the rim of a pot should be reserved for receiving water. Then insert the cutting to above the first node; if a leaf is attached to this node it is the only one that may be removed. Do not water again until the growing medium appears to be somewhat dry. Place the container where light will reach the cuttings but avoid hot sunshine, and maintain a moist environment. At night a temperature of 60 degrees is favorable. During the day the higher temperature caused by sun heat will be beneficial.

When cuttings have been rooted in flats or pans of sand, or a mixture of sand and peatmoss, they may be transplanted into pots as soon as their roots are a half inch long.

As soon as a small pot is filled with roots, a geranium of any kind should be transplanted to a three-, four-, or even a five-inch pot, the variety and condition of the plant determining the size. (For further details of potting procedure, see page 151.) When the plants show that they are well established and have reached four to six inches in height, it is time to pinch them back to shape the plants. Nipping out the tiny rolled tip of the stem, particularly on the garden geranium, on *Pelargonium domesticum*, also ivy-leaved geraniums, and large scented leaved kinds, induces branching and encourages the production of more flowers from the branches. Pinching should be done at least two months before the flowering season so that flowering will not be delayed. However, most pelargoniums will grow naturally if given sufficient room to spread.

For May flowers on *P. domesticum*, the plants should not be repotted after January or early February. For shapely plants three or four stems are usually allowed. As growth develops, pinching should be done to form a bushy plant. All weak shoots should be removed and, if the plant is too dense, center branches should be cut out to admit light to all parts of the plant. Pinching must be discontinued as soon as flowering stems appear about the end of February. In cool regions *P. domesticum* are essentially greenhouse plants and are purchased from nurserymen in bud or flower for house decoration or bedding out where climate permits. Where they are grown outdoors the year around, they attain the size of large shrubs.

NEW PLANTS FROM SEED

Pelargoniums are raised from seed mainly when new forms are being sought from hybrids. Seeds are also used when additional plants of a species are desired and cuttings or rooted stock are not readily obtainable.

Seedlings of hybrids rarely breed true to the parent type. Variations may occur in flower colors, leaf form, plant size, or branching habit. An occasional seedling may resemble a known or unsuspected ancestor. (The ancestry becomes obvious when, for example, a seedling of a garden geranium sends out arching stems or shows the colorful veining in flower petals characteristic of the ivy geranium.) Or a

completely new combination of traits may appear. That is why seeds
of the hybrids (cultivars) in one's collection should be used only
when one is deliberately seeking new variants. (For hybridizing, see
Chapter 5 of Part III, commencing on page 168.) Once a distinctive
new form has been derived from seed, the only way to duplicate the
new plant's characteristics is by vegetative propagation; that is, by
means of cuttings (page 147).

Seeds of the true species, on the other hand, can be expected to
give plants which replicate the parent. Except for those described in
Chapter 4 of Part II (commencing on page 101), relatively few
species of *Pelargonium* are in cultivation.

It takes longer to bring plants to the flowering stage from seed
than when starting them from cuttings. While some kinds will
bloom in six months, the majority wait two or three months longer,
and a few require up to two years of vegetative growth before they
will flower.

Seed Sowing

For sowing seeds of pelargoniums, the medium may consist of
equal parts of peatmoss and sand or of leafmold and sand. Or a
richer combination may be used by adding a fine grade of loam.
When peatmoss or leafmold and sand are used alone, transplanting
will need to be done sooner than when good garden loam is included
in the mixture. It is advisable to sterilize soil mixtures for growing
seedlings.

Either a flat or a shallow flowerpot known as a pan may be used as
a container. When deep pots are used a few layers of crock may be
placed in the bottom to conserve some of the soil mixture. Then the
pot may be filled with the sterilized soil to within a half inch of its
top or rim, and the whole watered thoroughly and allowed to drain
before sowing the seeds. The soil should be smoothed but not packed.
The seeds should be sown thinly and evenly on the surface and
pressed down lightly with a flat piece of dry wood. They should
then be covered with not more than a quarter inch of finely sifted
soil and sprinkled very gently with water to settle this soil around
the seeds.

After the seeds are sown the busy gardener may find it convenient
to cover the container with a pane of glass to reduce the necessity of

too frequent watering. If glass is used, the container should not be exposed to the direct rays of the sun, but there should be abundant light. As soon as germination begins, which is normally in about eight to ten days (though some varieties have been known to germinate after two years), the glass should be permanently removed so that the seedlings may have air. The soil should be kept moist, and watering should be carefully done so as not to dislodge the seedlings by washing away the soil from their little roots.

If the seeds are sown too thickly, the seedlings will have to be thinned out or transplanted sooner than should be necessary. If thin sowing is practiced, there will be enough space between the tiny plants to allow a free circulation of air and permit the natural spreading of their leaves.

Seedlings may be transplanted into small pots after they have attained a little size. If they are grown in a soil mixture containing garden loam, the gardener or nurseryman may transplant them at his convenience in a soil mixture used for mature plants. The size of the container to be used depends upon the type and size of pelargonium to be potted. The roots spread and penetrate downward, so the flowerpot should be large enough to allow for this further development.

Potting and Planting

In potting young seedlings or newly rooted cuttings, as in the subsequent repotting of mature pelargoniums, it is important to provide drainage by placing a piece or two of crock over the hole in the bottom of the pot. Then the pot should be partially filled with soil. The next step is to hold the plant in place at the desired height and fill in with the necessary amount of soil, pressing the plant firmly into place with the fingers, but not packing the soil hard. In small pots a space of half an inch should be allowed between the surface of the soil and the rim of the pot to provide for watering. In large pots there should be more space. Once the pot of soil is thoroughly watered, it is best not to water it again until the soil is almost dry.

After the young plants have been moved to small pots, their growth under favorable conditions is rapid. Soon they are in need of more root room and more space in which to spread their tops. Further transplanting becomes necessary, and they are transferred to larger containers. This potting is only one of many to which a pelargonium is subjected when it is not grown in the open ground throughout the year. It is an important phase of pelargonium culture that the grower must master to insure the well-being of his plants.

It may be just as harmful to repot a plant not in need of a change as it is to neglect a plant that is ready for repotting. The important thing is to know *when* repotting is necessary. Usually a pelargonium needs such attention at one of three different times:

1—At the beginning of the growing season. This generally means spring.

2—As often thereafter during the active growing season as the roots are seen to form a rather dense network around the outside of the soil ball, next to the inside of the pot. Only plants that are nearing the culminating stage in which they are to be enjoyed should be permitted to become potbound. By this is meant, for example, *P. hortorum* varieties on Memorial Day or *P. domesticum* varieties at Easter, when these are established in the largest pots they are to occupy.

3—When the plant is obviously ailing because of the soil in which it is planted. This often happens when the plants have been seriously overpotted or have been over-watered for any length of time.

Pots for growing pelargoniums should be clean. Clay pots are generally used. Glazed or painted pots are especially useful for terrace or patio plants where sun heat and wind tend to dry out the soil too rapidly from porous containers. The use of new pots is unnecessary if the old ones are well cleansed inside and outside, or if they are sterilized. All new clay pots should be soaked in water before use or they will absorb water from the soil, thereby depriving the roots of moisture.

As a general rule, in transplanting pelargoniums, pots only one size larger than the previous one should be used. Under some circumstances a pot of the same size or even smaller than the one in which the specimen has been growing will prove desirable. This situation arises with plants that have suffered from previous overpotting, and with sickly plants that have a poor root growth. The point to stress is that the new pot should comfortably contain the whole mass of healthy roots with ample but not excessive space around it for new soil.

Should the roots become potbound, the plants can usually be loosened by tapping the rim of the pot sharply on the edge of a table or bench while the plant is held upside down. Poking a stick through the drainage hole may also help. To provide the maximum amount of new soil, the root ball should be crushed to loosen and shake off as much of the old soil as possible.

When plants that have been semidormant, or at least resting, are given their first potting at the beginning of their growing season, they should generally be shaped by pruning. The cuttings may then be used for increasing stock. This treatment is especially applied to large *P. hortorum, P. domesticum*, scented-leaved and ivy-leaved varieties. At the same time some judicious root pruning also may be done.

When dealing with healthy specimens about to come into flower, it is better to feed them and defer repotting until the flowering period is over.

All plants should be thoroughly soaked with water a few hours before repotting so that the soil about the roots at potting time is moist but not muddy. The plant should be set slightly lower in the new pot than in the previous one. The space between the old root ball and the pot should be packed firmly with the new soil. Then new soil is added to the surface of the pot until it comes slightly above the old soil line around the stems.

Immediately after repotting, the plants should be watered very thoroughly. Subsequent watering, until the roots have taken hold in the new soil, must be done with good judgment to avoid both excessive dryness and extreme wetness in the soil. Newly potted pelargoniums, particularly if root disturbance has been at all marked, should be protected from drafts and shaded from sunshine for a few days to a week before restoring them to their normal environment.

Whether for a permanent planting where the climate is warm or for a one-season border or bed in cooler regions, the planting of pelargoniums outdoors does not differ much from the setting out of other bedding or herbaceous plants. First, the ground should be well prepared. The plants should be well watered an hour or two previously. The roots must not be unduly exposed to the wind, sunshine, or other drying conditions. When put in the ground the soil should be pressed firmly about the roots, and the plants should be thoroughly watered as soon as possible after they are planted. The need for subsequent watering will depend upon prevailing weather conditions. If a dull or showery day can be selected for planting, so much the better.

Chapter 3

GROWTH CONTROL

In all climates and all situations of culture—house, greenhouse, or outdoors—the pruning of geraniums results in healthier, more floriferous, and more shapely plants. Under different situations this practice may consist of the mere pinching out of terminal growth, the trimming out of leaves and shoots, or the drastic removal of large branches. The amount and length of growth to be cut out depends upon the type of plant, its size, age, condition, and environment. Dwarf, low, and slow-growing types are the only exceptions—and even these are often better looking after a discreet job of pinching back. With all others, good grooming of plants demands attention to pruning. If geraniums in the form of miniature trees are wanted, a precise program of pruning must be undertaken. (For details, see page 156.)

PRUNING FOR IMPROVED APPEARANCE

Unrestrained growth of geraniums is by no means synonymous with good appearance. In California, where plants grown outdoors throughout the year attain large size, it is just as important to practice methodical pruning on pelargoniums as it is on roses or shrubby perennials. The garden geraniums especially need this attention. Weak stems and branches, also old stems that have lost their vigor, should be cut away to enable the plants to give their energy to the

154

younger, healthier growth. This is best done after flowering. Trimming of tops and sides to control the shape may be safely done at any time, except that such work should be drastically reduced when the plant is ready to flower. The growth of flowering branches is encouraged by thinning out the centers of plants whose foliage has become extremely dense, as is apt to happen with the shrubby pelargoniums.

The Lady Washington type requires less severe pruning than the others. Where these are grown outdoors all year, some pruning may be done in fall, with additional trimming in spring only to remove any branches damaged by frost.

Where plants are bedded out in summer in the northern states pruning is a prelude to their transfer to winter quarters. They must be dug up before the first frost arrives, for they are very tender. Some of the roots are then pruned away, also a number of branches, until a shapely, compact framework for new growth is achieved.

Plants grown in pots are also in need of pruning in the fall. On these the parts removed will not be so large or numerous as on the more rampant plants that have been grown in the open ground.

For shapely potted plants of *P. domesticum*, Mr. R. M. Henley, Indiana specialist, recommends that only three or four stems be allowed to a plant. As growth develops, the pinching back of terminal growth should be practiced to induce a bushy form. All weak shoots are removed. If a plant becomes too dense the center branches are cut out to admit light and air to all remaining parts. The stopping of terminal growth by pinching should be discontinued as soon as flowering stems appear. In his Indiana greenhouses this is usually about the end of February. Compact, bushy plants with leaves to the ground, he points out, are possible only when plants are spaced and pruned so that light will reach all the foliage.

Many varieties of garden geraniums (*P. hortorum*) grow to large size and become woody in stems and branches. Such plants should be cut back vigorously after their flowering season, all woody parts except the main stem being removed. When new growth begins the tips of the branches should be nipped out to induce further branching and the subsequent formation of more flower clusters.

Large scented-leaved pelargoniums are grown chiefly for the scent and decorative value of their leaves, especially for flower arrangements. The frequent cutting of branches for these purposes will keep the plants in shape so that only old wood will need to be occasionally removed.

Young ivy geraniums planted along sidewalks in California soon cover their beds densely with foliage. Consequently and fortunately there is very little evaporation of moisture from the soil, and this lessens the need for artificial watering. Their natural habit of growth combined with the more or less constant moisture at their roots enables them to ramble on and on with vegetative, or leafy, growth. Regular pruning and pinching of branches must be done to increase the production of flowers and to avoid tangled masses when these plants are used as ground covers. Old woody stems must be removed from time to time to keep the beds level, otherwise they will form unsightly mounds. When grown in other situations pruning is equally necessary to avoid the appearance of leafless old wood that has outlived its usefulness.

Regular removal of old wood, cutting back of branches, nipping out the ends of new shoots and branches, and thinning of dense plants will give shape and beauty to all types of pelargoniums.

GERANIUMS IN TREE FORM

In the house where there is space, in the year-round greenhouse, or in regions where the plants may be kept outdoors, garden geraniums may be grown in tree form, sometimes referred to as "standards." The procedure is quite simple but, to grow a tall plant with a bushy head, it requires patience and watchfulness. Only the strongest growers with sturdy stems are suitable for this purpose; if slender stemmed varieties are selected, they will need support by staking. All side shoots should be removed right from the cutting stage, and only one stem (two at the most) allowed to grow on. Rapid growth should be encouraged until the required height is attained; then the head is allowed to form. To make the head dense and highly productive of flowers, the branches in the head itself may now be pinched back at the tip. When a tree pelargonium has served as an outdoor ornament in one of the northern states, it may be housed for the winter in a sunny window without being transplanted from its tub. In climates where there is no danger of damage from cold weather, a geranium tree may be kept growing outdoors all winter long.

Chapter 4

PESTS, OTHER TROUBLES, AND REMEDIES

Some of the troubles affecting pelargoniums are the direct result of bad cultural practices, such as the crowding of the plants, lack of fresh air, insufficient light, or too much moisture. While such conditions will directly affect the plants' growth and appearance, they will also facilitate attack by pests and infectious diseases.

Even though pelargoniums were long considered relatively free from troubles, they have been found to be as susceptible as other plants to pests that live above the soil or in it, and also by bacterial, fungus, and virus diseases. It is therefore advisable to learn to recognize symptoms, to know what preventive measures one can take, and what remedies are available, once troubles strike.

INSECTS AND THEIR KIN

Each part of the country has its own major problems, particularly with such pests as nematodes, slugs, and insects of various kinds which may be common in one region and unknown in another. An unanticipated invasion can be disastrous in a commercial planting. The home gardener, however, having fewer plants and less at stake, is likely to have fewer troubles. But wherever plants are grown, knowledge and alertness will help in discerning and controlling pests.

157

Nematodes

A destructive pest that sometimes attacks pelargoniums is the microscopic root nematode, or eelworm, which is prevalent in outdoor plantings in the southern states from the Atlantic to the Pacific coast and up into Oregon. In the northern states where cold weather freezes the ground it is regarded more as a greenhouse pest.

Nematodes cause the disease known as root knot. They occur in swellings which sometimes appear on the roots or at the base of a stem just below the surface of the soil.

If the infestation is mild, the plants may be merely sickly and stunted; if severe, pelargoniums are killed. If the parasite is suspected but not evident in a rare plant, one may take cuttings and plant them in sterilized soil. Their condition will need to be carefully watched, however, if a new infestation is to be avoided.

Badly infested plants must be destroyed, and the soil in which they grew must be sterilized before it can be safely used again for planting. Baking or steaming is advised. Chemical sterilizers such as MC2, ethylene dibromide, or chloropicrin are available. If proper precautions are taken these chemicals are safe to use, providing the directions on the package are followed implicitly. Furthermore, when chemicals of this nature are used for sterilizing, the soil may not be used for plants for two days if treated with MC2, and about three weeks for the others.

Soil Mealy Bug

This pest also lives in the soil, where it feeds on the juices of the fibrous root systems of plants. Fortunately, it is not widespread and can be easily eradicated in pots, but not so easily in field plantings. Drenching the soil with dichlorethyl ether will destroy the mealy bugs themselves. Their larvae, however, will require a second or third application for complete destruction. This treatment should be tried on a small scale until it has been determined that there will be no injury to geraniums. In addition, the plants should not be suffering from lack of water when application is made or injury is more likely to occur.

Caterpillars

The larval stages of several kinds of moths may damage geraniums. Among the most common are the greenhouse leaf tier, the orange tortrix, and the tobacco budworm. The caterpillars of the greenhouse leaf tier and the orange tortrix are similar in appearance, both being whitish, yellowish, or greenish and about three-quarters of an inch long when full grown. While both species roll or tie the leaves together with a fine white web, the orange tortrix often bores into flower buds and terminal shoots as well. The larvae of other moths commit similar damage.

The caterpillar of the tobacco budworm varies considerably in color, but is usually light green or pinkish with pale longitudinal stripes. It is about one to one and one-half inches long when full grown, and feeds upon both flowers and leaves, giving them a ragged appearance. It may also bore into the tender terminal shoots.

Frequent inspection of plants is advisable in preventing damage from these pests. A spray of DDT will control most of the caterpillars attacking geraniums, but it is not effective against the orange tortrix. Therefore, either DDD or malathion should be used against this pest. A combination of DDT and malathion will keep plants free of almost every other pest as well.

Weevils

A small black-mouthed beetle with yellow specks on its wings has been known to attack geraniums in winter. This is the black vine weevil whose larvae are apparently brought in with the soil. From the roots on which the larvae feed, they work up into the crown and emerge as beetles on the leaves. The Fuller rose beetle is also reported to attack geraniums. For control spray with DDT-malathion.

Ants

While ants do not attack plants themselves, they are associated with aphids because these excrete a sweetish substance (called honeydew) which is enjoyed by ants. Aphids, which can be serious pests, are carried from plant to plant by the ants. Chlordane sprays and dusts will effectively control ants.

Aphids

These small green louselike insects are found in clusters near the tips of young shoots. If permitted to live and reproduce unchecked, they will invade the leaves and flowers. Often they act as carriers of virus disease. To destroy aphids spray with malathion or lindane.

Mealy Bugs

Perhaps the most annoying pests of plants grown in the window garden are the mealy bugs. These are whitish woolly relatives of aphids. They deposit their eggs in woolly masses and the young migrate over the plants and form new colonies. They usually attach themselves to the end of a leaf stalk where it joins the stem, along the tips of new growth, or along the veins on the undersurface of the leaves. One or two thorough applications of malathion will destroy the insects and their eggs.

Whitefly

The very small whitish winged insect which is known as whitefly has already done most of its damage when it first becomes evident. The small, flat, scalelike bodies of the immature stages are scarcely noticeable on the undersides of the leaves. But the quantity of juices that these insects suck from the plant bring about a serious loss of vigor. Growers of *P. domesticum* are especially troubled with whitefly. Adults and young can both be controlled with a DDT-malathion spray.

Mites

So small that they are barely visible to the naked eye, mites nevertheless distort stems, leaves, and often flowers if the infestation is severe. Before the flowers are attacked, a brownish network caused by the feeding of the mites will be noticeable on the leaves, followed by corky streaks along the veins. Spraying with malathion or aramite will give effective control. In warm areas, especially where plants are subject to reinfestation, more than one application may be required, especially with malathion, which does not have the residual effect of lindane.

Thrips

Minute insects that feed on the juices of many kinds of plants, occasionally trouble pelargoniums. To control them spray with DDT-malathion, malathion alone or lindane.

Termites

Where termites (white ants) are present around wooden structures, they may take advantage of the woody stems of pelargoniums as tunneling areas. They enter through the soil, which they reach through the drainage hole of potted plants. The plants are likely to yellow and die when termites are feeding in the stem. To prevent damage to uninfested plants, a chlordane spray may be used on the surrounding soil.

Snails and Slugs

Metaldehyde dust will control slugs. Metaldehyde baits are effective against snails. Clean culture and good sanitation are also important.

Commercial growers may use certain insecticides which are not safe for home use, such as parathion or TEPP. The DDT-malathion combination should control practically all pests, and is simple and safe to use if normal precautions, which should be followed with all insecticides, are taken.

FUNGUS AND BACTERIAL DISEASES

Blossoms, leaves, stems, and roots of pelargoniums all are subject to attacks by various fungi and bacteria. A dark spotting or a soft rotting of the part affected is the usual symptom. These diseases generally occur only when the plants are crowded, when the soil is kept too wet, or when the atmosphere is cold, sunless, and damp for a prolonged period.

The obvious preventive measures are to keep the plants well spaced in a light, airy situation and to give them just enough but not excessive water. Thorough but infrequent waterings are healthier than a daily soaking of the roots. For plants grown indoors, sterilization of soil is a help in disease prevention, for some diseases, as well as certain insects, otherwise will live over in the soil.

Where disease does strike (and fortunately it does not come frequently), five courses are imperative for the grower: (1) to correct the conditions of culture; (2) to remove and burn immediately all infected parts—or the plants themselves, if need be—always taking care not to spread the disease by touching or letting disease spores fall upon healthy plants; (3) to spray or dust the remaining plants with Bordeaux mixture or some other fungicide; (4) to sterilize all tools that have come in contact with diseased plants (see next page); (5) to water each pot separately and carefully, as splashing water and flying soil particles are very likely to cause the spread of the disease.

Stem-Rot and Leaf-Spot

These two troublesome and enigmatic bacterial diseases have lately been found to be caused by the same organism. When the leaves are affected the disease takes one form; when the stem is involved, the symptoms are somewhat different. The bacterium, *Xanthomonas pelargonii*, also causes serious losses of cuttings. The chief victim of the disease is the garden geranium, *Pelargonium hortorum. P. domesticum* is said to be resistant.

In *Geraniums Around the World*, the publication of the International Geranium Society (Volume 2, Number 3, 1954), the leaf-spot stage of this disease is described in part as follows:

"Small, water-soaked areas 1–3 mm. in diameter appear on the underside of the leaf and occasionally on the upper surface. The spots enlarge and become more conspicuous and in several days a small water-soaked area may be formed around the edges of the spot in the shape of a 'halo.' In several days the spot becomes brown and sunken and dry. If there are very many spots on a leaf the whole leaf becomes yellow and withers and drops from the plant."

The stem-rot stage may or may not follow the infection of the leaves. The description of this is as follows:

"Infected stems are blackened and shriveled externally, and when split lengthwise a black semi-dry rot is evident. There may be black streaks on the non-rotted portions of the stems which show the presence of the bacteria in the vascular system. The other characteristic symptom is the upright, almost completely defoliated appearance of large plants. Only the terminals of the branches have leaves and they are usually quite small. The plant is difficult to uproot in the early stages. . . . Usually plants die within 3 months after the first symptoms."

The cutting-rot stage (which, it is pointed out, is microscopically distinct from the rot caused by the fungus, *Pythium*) progresses somewhat slowly from the base upward. The cutting shrivels and becomes dull black (not shiny black as in *Pythium*). Cutting tools, water, soil or other rooting medium, and infected neighboring plants all spread the disease rapidly.

Since this rot is highly infectious it is almost impossible to control it, once it starts, by using sprays and dusts. Complete destruction of infected leaves or plants is a required safeguard. When removing them it is a good idea to use a paper bag kept tightly closed as a repository until the diseased material can be burned. Soil that has not been used for geraniums for at least six months—or preferably a year is recommended as one means of prevention. Cutting tools can be safely disinfected with 70% methyl alcohol. After infected plants have been destroyed, remaining plants may be sprayed with one of several fungicides, such as bordeaux mixture (4–2–100) or bioquin to prevent further spread of the disease.

Fungus Leaf-Spot

Circular spots of light reddish brown with dark brown borders distinguish the fungus leaf-spot caused by *Cercospora* from the sunken, sometimes darker-centered spots of the bacterial infection described above. Still another spotting of leaves is occasionally caused by the fungus *Alternaria*. The same directions for control apply to all of these bacterial and fungus diseases—propagation from disease-free plants, improved conditions of culture as to soil, humidity, temperature, and ventilation, complete destruction of diseased parts, fungicidal treatment of remaining plants, sterilization of tools, and extreme care in watering.

Black Leg

Pythium stem rot, commonly known as black leg, occurs mainly on cuttings, although mature plants are sometimes infected. Like the bacterial stem rot, this fungus infection starts at the base and works upward, the leaves quickly wilting and dying. To prevent it, cuttings should be taken only from healthy plants and only a sterilized rooting medium should be used. If plants become infected, they should of course be immediately and cautiously destroyed. If uninfected ones are left in a flat, they should be transferred at once to a new sterilized area.

Botrytis Blight

Water-soaked brown areas on leaves and blossoms soon become covered with grayish spores when *Botrytis* is present. This disease is particularly prevalent under conditions of coolness with high humidity. Botrytis and alternaria leaf spot fungi live on dead tissues and grow from dead to living portions of the plant. Prompt removal of dead flowers, leaves, branches and debris will decrease the number of spores in an area. Spraying with captan (two pounds to a hundred gallons of water) at five- to seven-day intervals is helpful.

Wilt

The soil fungus *Verticillium* occasionally infects geraniums, causing the lower leaves to turn yellow from the margins inward, eventually wilting completely. Shoots may become stunted. Plants should be destroyed to prevent the spread of the fungus, and the soil in which they grew should be sterilized before it is used again. The latest recommendation for sterilizing soil six inches deep and ten inches across is an injection of 2 cubic centimeters of chloropicrin, or methyl bromide (four pounds to a hundred square feet) may be used.

VIRUS DISEASES

In greenhouses and in commercial fields where many plants are grown together, viruses can be vicious invaders. Keeping them at bay is a major problem of large-scale growers, for if they start spreading through a planting, one might as well say good-bye to all the plants. If a rare variety is about to be lost and if the virus has not yet reached the entire plant, it may be possible to grow a new stock of plants from healthy-looking tips. These should be isolated from other plants and carefully watched. If they develop symptoms of virus after they have rooted, they must be immediately destroyed.

There is as yet no dust or spray that will halt an infection by a virus. Viruses can be avoided (1) by using true seed in propagating, since none of the geranium viruses are known to be transmitted in this way, and (2) by initially selecting virus-free stocks when they are to be used to obtain cuttings.

Leaf Curl

This virus, known also as crinkle-leaf, is characterized by irregular or circular pale yellow to white spots up to one-fourth inch in diameter. Often the leaves are ruffled, crinkled, dwarfed, or malformed.

Mosaic

Light and dark mottling of the leaves and dwarfing of the plants give evidence of mosaic. This virus disease is less severe than leaf curl. It is often confused with nutritional imbalances. Continuous and vigorous destruction of infected plants will almost eliminate the trouble.

PHYSIOLOGICAL TROUBLES

Faulty conditions of culture or unfavorable weather can be as devastating as viruses, bacteria, fungi or insects. Such manifestations are known as physiological diseases.

Edema

Common among physiological troubles is edema or dropsy. This occurs in greenhouses or in windows that are overcrowded with plants, and has somewhat the effect of leaf spot, with water-soaked areas that become rusty then corky. The ailing plants respond to the same good cultural practices that help to repel the invasion of fungus diseases—plenty of air and light, without too much water.

Failure to Flower

In *P. domesticum* varieties, poor flowering is likely to be the result of growing plants in temperatures above 60 degrees at night. In *P. hortorum* varieties it may be caused by late pinching, low temperatures, low light intensity, lack of water during the growing season, or lack of nutrients in the soil. All of these factors contribute to delayed growth and delayed flowering. *P. peltatum* varieties require temperatures above 55 degrees for successful flowering. *P. hortorum* varieties also do best with this temperature as a minimum.

Marginal Drying of Leaves

Potash deficiency in the soil is likely to cause the leaves to dry around the edges. Feeding with a balanced fertilizer high in potash content will remedy the trouble.

Light Green Leaves

When light coloring is unnatural in a variety, nitrogen deficiency is indicated. Ammonium sulphate or some other form of quickly available nitrogen in weak solution is the cure. Several light applications of the fertilizer are preferred to a single dose of greater concentration. A complete chemical fertilizer high in nitrogen in weak solution is also helpful.

Dark Green, Dwarfed Leaves

When leaves are abnormally dark in color and small in size, a phosphorus deficiency is indicated. Feeding the plants with superphosphate in solution will give the leaves normal color and size.

Reddening of Leaves

A combination of factors may cause reddening of the leaves followed by drying of the foliage at the base of the plant. Low atmospheric temperature, low soil temperature in spring, and a low supply of nitrogen all play a part. Correction of the faulty environment— or waiting for it to correct itself, so far as outside temperature is concerned—will restore the plants to normal.

Legginess

Lanky plants with sparse foliage at the base are often the result of crowding and insufficient sunlight. For well grown, bushy plants it is necessary to space them more widely as soon as they begin to crowd and expose them to more sunlight. Legginess is also sometimes caused by inherited traits. When this is true, if the form of the plant is displeasing, a different variety can be substituted.

Chapter 5

HYBRIDIZATION

Before hybridization of plants was understood, most of the new
forms which arose among them were the result of cross-pollination
carried on by insects or the wind. In the early history of pelargoniums,
chance hybridization of plants in cultivation gave to gardens such outstanding plants as *P. scarboroviae, P. blandfordianum* and 'Scarlet
Unique.' Many others, too, arose without the aid of man as a hybridist.
Then, as growers gradually learned how to control the crossing, more
and more unique and handsome forms were created. With one, the
aim would be coloration on the leaves; with another, larger flowers,
doubling of petals, new colors and combinations. Fragrance has
sometimes been the objective; miniature forms another aim.

Despite the hundreds of fine cultivars (hybrids) that are available
today, it is always a challenge to the amateur gardener as well as the
commercial grower to develop his own cultivars. Cross-pollination is a
simple process, and when the resulting seedlings come into bloom,
the hybridist may have realized his desire for a plant that differs from
all others. A problem may arise in finding space for these new plants,
for, in the attempt to achieve the desired hybrid, each seedling should
be raised to the flowering stage. Otherwise the prize may be among
the discarded seedlings.

In hybridizing, there should be a definite aim in mind, such as a
large long lasting flower cluster of purest white with a single whorl
of broad, indented petals, on a sturdy plant that blossoms early.
Parents with as many of these qualities as possible should then be
selected. Actually, new qualities do not arise spontaneously during

hybridization. It is only the intensifying and recombination of certain characteristics of the parents that make them appear as new.

Some pelargoniums do not set seeds. It would be useless to use one of this kind as the seed parent in a cross. If its stamens bear noticeable pollen and if it has the desired characteristics, it might serve as the pollen parent for a hybrid.

A question frequently asked by the beginning gardener is: "Can a geranium be crossed with a pelargonium?" If the garden geranium (*P. hortorum*) is referred to, the answer is generally yes, although members of this group do not breed readily with the pelargoniums of gardeners (*P. domesticum*). With certain other limitations, in which species are said to be incompatible, almost any plant in the genus *Pelargonium* can be crossed with another. But if a plant of the genus *Geranium*, such as the familiar wild geranium of our northern woodlands, is in the inquirer's mind, then the answer is no. So far as is known, no plant of the genus *Geranium* has yet been crossed with a plant of the genus *Pelargonium*. The relationship between the two groups is not quite close enough. (For the distinction between these two genera, see Part I, Chapter 4.)

The hybridizing process is very simple. To make a cross the powdery pollen is taken from a flower of one selected plant and dusted on the sticky stigma of a flower on the plant chosen as the seed parent. It is best to use a small camel's hair brush for transferring the pollen from one flower to another.

When selecting the seed parent one should make sure that the pollen on its flowers is not ripe—that is, not powdery—or it will cling to the brush with the originally selected pollen. When this happens it is best to sterilize the brush by dipping it into alcohol and allowing it to dry before using it again. Or, better yet, for extra precaution, also to avoid self-pollination, it is advisable to remove the anthers in advance from the flowers to be pollinated. If the plants are grown in an open field or where winds or flying insects are prevalent, a further precaution against undesirable pollination is to tie a bag (cheesecloth, paper, or cellophane) around each flower that has been artificially pollinated.

Seeds will be ready for planting any time after the ovary, now become a dry seed capsule, splits open to release them. (For directions for seed sowing see page 150.)

The methodical hybridist will keep a record of each cross and of the resulting seedlings. If he has the rare good luck of producing the flower of his dreams, it will be a double satisfaction if he knows and can say to his inquiring horticultural friends: "My Dream' is a cross between this and that pelargonium. Here is the record of its parentage."

Chapter 6

GERANIUMS IN THE SMALL GREENHOUSE

Gardening is a delightful adventure for gardeners who possess a greenhouse where they can pursue their activities indoors when the beauty of the outdoor garden has waned after the first frost of autumn. The greenhouse may contain plants transferred from the outdoor garden and others which are maintained under glass the year around.

MOVING AND PRUNING

Bedding geraniums may be brought into the greenhouse before the first frost; in the vicinity of Philadelphia and New York City, it is advisable to give them shelter before the end of October.

Large, bushy pelargoniums that have been growing in the open ground, and have finished their flowering for the season, and that are to be brought into the greenhouse, will need to be prepared for potting. The stems of large plants such as those of *P. denticulatum* may be pruned back more than stems of smaller pelargoniums; the branches should be cut also, and long roots should be cut off with sharp shears at the same time. Pruning of stems and branches will induce further branching and, consequently, more flower clusters, and make the plant more shapely. The stems and branches of flowering geraniums should not be pruned, but it may be necessary to cut off some of the roots if they are too long for proper placing in the required size of container.

After pruning the cuttings may be used for rooting. The ensuing plants will be excellent for bedding out the following spring. After the pruned parent plants have rested for four to six weeks they will make rapid growth. Assuming that the plants were well grown in the first place and were productive of flowers all summer, they will begin to flower again about the end of January. These plants may be transferred to flower beds the following spring without ill effects, and they will continue to flower all summer. This procedure may be continued until the plants are five or six years old, or until the stems become too woody and the branches crowded. By this time the leaves and flowers will have decreased in size and quantity and it is advisable then to discard the old plants and replace them with younger ones raised from their cuttings.

There is a great advantage in taking cuttings as by this means good plants can be perpetuated and the stock increased. In this way garden geraniums can be raised almost any month of the year so flowering specimens are available at all times. The average flowering period of the garden geranium grown in the open ground in the vicinity of Philadelphia is about six to seven months if they are properly cared for. Garden and ivy geraniums will begin to flower soon after cuttings have been well rooted. At this stage the plants will be small, but they will continue to flower in the greenhouse if growing conditions are right. For flowering plants in late autumn and early winter, cuttings should be rooted in June to July; for late winter and early spring flowering plants, cuttings should be rooted in late August or September. In either case summer cuttings taken from *P. hortorum*, *P. peltatum*, and scented-leaved kinds may be rooted in the greenhouse or in a sheltered part of the garden in the open ground. These young plants are excellent for bedding out the following spring and will flower all summer.

SELECTION OF PLANTS FOR THE GREENHOUSE

The most popular varieties grown in private eastern greenhouses in winter include the salmon-pink-flowered 'Mrs. E. G. Hill'; the choice orange-flowered 'Maxime Kovalevski'; 'Mme. Landry' with intense salmon-pink flowers, and 'Dryden' with its gay, white-centered, light red flowers, which is particularly desirable because it is a persistent bloomer. These are all forms of *P. hortorum*.

Large, bushy, scented-leaved pelargoniums such as *P. denticulatum* and *P. graveolens* may need to be pruned back hard if they are to be

potted for the greenhouse. Small and slender growing kinds such as
P. *crispum* and its relatives may need pruning only for shaping them,
whereas low growing plants such as P. *fragrans* and P. *odoratissimum*
do not require pruning at all. Although the leaves of 'Fair Ellen' are
not sweet scented, this is, nevertheless, a choice subject for the
greenhouse because of its compact growing habit and its handsome
and distinctive flowers. Most scented-leaved pelargoniums do not
have a long flowering season, but this lack is compensated for by
their interesting and fragrant foliage, and the fernlike leaves of some
kinds adds an airy grace to the composite scene.

A few specimens of ivy-leaved pelargoniums seem almost necessary in the greenhouse for pleasing contrast of color and design. They
are particularly suited for growing in containers that can be sus-
pended from a height so that the branches can trail naturally downward. In this higher position the atmosphere is usually warmer and
airier so that they may need to be watered more often than they
otherwise would. When bringing them into the greenhouse the
long branches may be trimmed back to encourage the production of
more branches and flower clusters. The new branches will be shorter,
and they are not so apt to interfere with the plants growing beneath
them. When ivy-leaved pelargoniums are trained to grow over an
arched trellis framing a walk in a garden or greenhouse, they present
a colorful picture when in bloom. Though the lax stems and branches
of 'Scarlet Unique' and 'Rollisons Unique' do not grow as long as
those of ivy-leaved kinds, these plants with their brilliantly colored
flowers can be trained to grow on short, upright trellises. P. *peltatum*
varieties are as easy to propagate as the garden geranium, and the
abundant flower clusters will stud the container with a mass of color.

If space is available for deciduous pelargoniums that can be kept
quite dry during their resting period after they have shed their leaves,
there are a number of them that have decorative possibilities when in
leaf and flower. Among these are the spiny stemmed and handsome
flowered P. *echinatum* and P. *stapletonii*.

P. *domesticum* varieties are essentially greenhouse plants except in
favored climates where they are usually grown in the open ground all
year, or as potted terrace or patio plants. The stems of these plants
are woodier than those of the garden geranium and, consequently,
cuttings take longer to root. In eastern greenhouses some commercial

growers feed selected plants once a month with weak fertilizer for two or three months to encourage the plants to vegetate and produce softer wood for propagation. Lacking greenhouse facilities, in cool regions it is advisable to purchase plants in bud or flower from a nurseryman if they are desired for house decoration.

Raising *P. domesticum* varieties in a greenhouse is worth the slight extra attention that is required by them because their flowers are very different from those of all other pelargoniums. They produce the largest flower clusters and largest florets and their decorative possibilities are unlimited. If lavender and purple tones are desired, they can be supplied by 'Lavender Queen' or 'Dieners Thirty-Three.' 'Mary Bard,' 'Onkel Richter' and 'Miss Saunders' have lightly marked white flowers. The flowers of 'Joan Fontaine' are striking, the edge of the petals being bright red and the center of each overlaid with a large brownish-black velvetlike blotch that is brought into bolder relief by the small amount of light color in the center of the floret. Plants with flowers of many other colors and color combinations are available for any other color scheme the gardener may desire.

GENERAL CARE

In managing a greenhouse there are five essential points for the gardener to remember if maximum results are to be achieved in growing pelargoniums. They are control of temperature, plenty of ventilation, careful watering, placing of plants where they will receive all the sunshine that is to be had during the short days of autumn and winter, and sanitation.

Pelargoniums require a cool greenhouse where the night temperature does not exceed 60 degrees. During the day the temperature will rise naturally 10 or 15 degrees, higher on sunny days. These temperatures are considered ideal for growing these plants.

On warm, clear days in autumn all ventilators and doors should be fully opened; on cold winter days a slight crack may be sufficient for a change of fresh circulating air. So important is fresh air to the welfare of the plants that a reduction in temperature for a short time is preferable to a stale or humid atmosphere. If a strong cold wind is blowing, and it is possible to admit air from the opposite side of the wind, it is wise to do so.

Other conditions being favorable, plants will make their best growth in soils that are uniformly supplied with a sufficient amount of moisture. This is best maintained by thorough watering at rather infrequent intervals. Both the amount of water and the frequency of application are matters that require good judgment (see page 143).

If gardening is continued in the greenhouse in summer, light and heat must be given further consideration. When the days lengthen and the sun becomes warmer, and before the intense light and heat of summer become unendurable for pelargoniums and the gardener, some form of shade must be provided. For a small greenhouse attached to a house a good device for this purpose is a roller type of shade made of narrow slats or strips of wood and attached to the outer side of the glass. This type of shade may be easily regulated by means of a pulley, and raised or lowered as the occasion demands. It is a decided advantage to unroll them over the glass on sunny days, and to roll them up on cool, cloudy days. If it is not possible to obtain roller shades, or if it is impractical for a small or large detached greenhouse, a satisfactory substitute is a coating of some suitable preparation applied on the outer side of the glass.

Various formulas are used for painting. One formula consists of gasoline into which a very small amount of white lead is stirred. If more than just enough white lead is used to color the gasoline, the mixture will adhere stubbornly to the glass, making it necessary to scrape it off as soon as more light is needed for the plants in autumn. Whitewash composed of slaked lime and water, to which bluing may be added if desired, is another preparation commonly used. If this preparation contains too much lime, it may adhere to the glass longer than is desired, and it will have to be scraped off or removed with a coarse brush and water.

The objective of the gardener is to grow healthy, disease-free pelargoniums, and to arrange them in an artistic manner so that they may be enjoyed when in full leaf and flower. To accomplish this the greenhouse must be kept clean to discourage the breeding of pests that seek dark places under the rubbish of discarded leaves or flowers. All dried up or decayed leaves and dead flowers should be removed from the plants and taken out of the greenhouse as soon as possible, preferably on the day that they are removed from the plants. Dead petals that have fallen on good leaves should likewise be removed so that the leaves do not become spotted. The surface soil of pots should be examined regularly for caking or mossy growth. If this has happened the mossy growths should be removed, and the crusty surfaces should be broken up, so that as much air as possible can reach the soil and keep it sweet. Plants should not be crowded together; each plant should be given enough space so that air and light can surround each one. It is better to grow a lesser number of plants so that each one may be a good specimen, rather than many plants that interfere with each other's development.

Arranging plants on two or more levels in a greenhouse creates a more artistic effect than when plants of approximately the same size are placed together on one level. If staging of boards is not feasible, inverted flower pots of various sizes can be placed at intervals along the bench, and on these foliage or flowering plants can be placed to show them off to better advantage.

Authorities

References are found in Chapter 5, Part I.

Ait.—William Aiton
Andr.—Henry C. Andrews
L. H. Bailey
L. Bolus—Louisa Bolus
Cav.—Antonio José Cavanilles
Curt.—William Curtis
DC.—Augustin Pyramus de Candolle
Dietr.—Friedrich Gottlieb Dietrich
Dinter—Moritz Kurt Dinter
R. A. Dyer—R. Allen Dyer
Erhr.—Friedrich Ehrhart
Fenzl—Eduard Fenzl
Harv.—William Henry Harvey
Haw.—Adrian Hardy Haworth
Hochst.—Christian Friedrich Hochstetter
Hoffmsgg.—Johann Centurius Hoffmannsegg
Hort.—Hortorum
Jacq.—Nicolaus Joseph von Jacquin
Jacq. f.—Joseph Franz von Jacquin
L.—Carl Linnaeus
L. f.—Carl von Linné, the younger
L'Hér.—Charles Louis L'Héritier
Lodd.—Conrad Loddiges
Mart.—K. F. P. von Martius
Mill.—Philip Miller
H. E. Moore—Harold E. Moore, Jr.
Pers.—Christian Hendrik Persoon
Schrank—Franz von Paula von Schrank
Sims—John Sims
Smith—Sir James Edward Smith
Sond.—Otto Sonder
Sprague—Thomas Archibald Sprague
Sweet—Robert Sweet
Voigt—Johann Otto Voigt
Wendl.—Johann Christoph Wendland
Willd.—Karl Ludwig Willdenow

177

References

AITON, WILLIAM. *Hortus Kewensis*. 1789.

ANDREWS, HENRY C. *Geraniums*. London, 1805.

BAILEY, LIBERTY HYDE. *Cyclopedia of American Horticulture*, 1900.

———. *The Standard Cyclopedia of Horticulture*. New York, 1914.

BURMAN, NICOLAUS L. *Specimen Botanicum de Geraniis*. Leyden, 1759.

DECANDOLLE, AUGUSTIN PYRAMUS. *Prodromus*. Switzerland, 1824.

DILLENIUS, JOHANN JACOB. *Hortus Elthamensis*. England, 1732.

FEDDE, PHILIP F. *Repertorium Specierum Novarum*. Berlin, 1920, 1923.

GERARD, JOHN. *The Herball*. 1597; another edition, enlarged by T. Johnson, 1633.

GRIEVE, PETER. *A History of Variegated Zonal Pelargoniums*. London, 1868.

HARVEY, WILLIAM H., and SONDER, OTTO W. *Flora Capensis*. Dublin, 1859–1860.

HOFFMANNSEGG, JOHANN CENTURIUS. *Verzeichniss der Pflanzenkulturen*. Dresden, 1824.

HOOKER, JOSEPH DALTON (editor). *Icones Plantarum*. London, 1880–1891.

HOOKER, WILLIAM JACKSON (editor). *Journal of Botany and Kew Garden Miscellany*. London, 1849–1857.

Index Kewensis, and *Supplements*. 1895–1953.

JACQUIN, NICOLAUS JOSEPH. *Icones Plantarum Rariorum*. 1781–1786, 1786–1793.

———. *Plantarum Rariorum Horti Caesarei Schoenbrunnensis*. Vienna, 1797–1804.

KNUTH, REINHARD. "Geraniaceae," in Engler, *Das Pflanzenreich*. IV, Vol. 129: 1912.

———. "Uber Bastardbildung in Der Gattung Pelargonium," *Botanische Jahrbücher von Engler*. Vol. 44: 1909.

L'HÉRITIER, CHARLES LOUIS. *Geraniologia*. Paris, 1787–1788 (1792).

MOORE, HAROLD E., JR. "Pelargoniums in Cultivation," *Baileya*. Ithaca, 1955.

POST, KENNETH. *Florist Crop Production and Marketing*. New York, 1950.

SWEET, ROBERT. *Geraniaceae*. England, 1820–1830.

Thomas Jefferson's Garden Book. American Philosophical Society, 1944.

TRATTINNICK, LEOPOLD. *Neue Arten von Pelargonien*. 1825–1831.

178

WENDLAND, J. C. *Hortus Herrenhusanus.* Hanover, 1789–1801.
WILLDENOW, CARL LUDWIG. *Enumeratio Plantarum.* Berlin, 1809.
———. *Hortus Berolinensis.* 1816.
———. (editor). Linnaeus' *Species Plantarum.* Edition 4, Vol. 3. Berlin, 1800.

Periodicals

American Florist. 1886–1918.
American Flower Garden Dictionary. Philadelphia, 1839.
American Gardener, The. 1823–1856.
American Gardeners Magazine. 1835–1864.
American Journal of Horticulture. 1867–1871.
Cottage Gardener, The. England, 1849–1860.
Curtis's Botanical Magazine. England, 1793–1946.
Floral Magazine. England, 1868–1880.
Floral World. England, 1867–1874.
Flore des Serres et des Jardins de l'Europe. Gent, 1847–1865.
Florist and Pomologist. 1875–1881.
Florists' Exchange. 1896–1917.
Florist and Horticultural Journal. Philadelphia, 1855.
Garden, The. England, 1872–1927.
Gardeners' Chronicle, The. London, 1841–1939.
Gardeners' Monthly. Thomas Meehan, Editor. 1865–1871.
Gartenflora. 1868–1927.
Geraniums Around the World, 1249 Redondo Beach Blvd., Gardena, Calif., current.
Hamburger Garten- und Blumenzeitung. 1852–1890.
Horticulteur Français. 1851–1873.
Horticulturist, The. England, 1846–1852.
Horticultural Journal of Rural Arts and Tastes. England, 1859–1861.
L'Illustration Horticole. Brussels, 1854–1878.
Philadelphia Florist. 1852–1853.
Revue de l'Horticulture Belge. Gent, 1862–1902.
Vick's Floral Guide. Rochester, New York, 1861–1885.
Vick's Illustrated Magazine. Rochester, New York, 1878–1890.
Western Horticultural Review. Cincinnati, Ohio, 1850–1853.
Wiener Illustrierte Gartenzeitung. 1880–1903.

Commercial Sources of Geranium (Pelargonium) Plants

Ace Nursery—2387–93 Lincoln Ave., Altadena, California. Fair selection, most types.

Antonelli Brothers—Capitola, California. Limited selection, all kinds.

Arndt, Milton H.—Carlton Villa, 600 Etra Road, Hightstown, New Jersey. Extensive collection of all types.

Bells Geranium Garden—221 West 223rd St., Torrance, Calif. Large selection, all types.

Brigham, Dorcas—Village Hill Nursery, Williamsburg, Mass. Species, rare hybrids, scented-leaved, selected list of others.

Brown The Florist—Fond du Lac, Wis. Mostly P. hortorum.

Germain's—747 Terminal St., Los Angeles 21, Calif. Selective list, hortorum, peltatum, and domesticum.

Geraniumtown—P. O. Box 89, Santa Paula. Extensive list of all types.

Hallowell's Seed Co.—San Francisco 5, Calif. P. hortorum, domesticum, and peltatum plants.

Havalook Gardens—Fowlerville, Mich. Selected list various types.

Henley, R. M.—1510 S. Walnut St., Hartford City, Ind. Specialist in P. domesticum.

Howard, Paul J.—11700 National Blvd., Los Angeles 24, Calif. P. hortorum, domesticum and peltatum varieties.

Henry Field Seed & Nursery Co.—Shenandoah, Iowa. Selected list P. hortorum, domesticum, and peltatum.

Horner's Nursery—1730–50 N Ave., National City, Calif. Large selection, all types.

Leatherman's Gardens—El Monte, Calif. P. hortorum, domesticum and scented-leaved varieties.

Miller, Holmes C.—250 West Portola, Los Altos, Calif. Specialist in P. hortorum varieties.

Merry Gardens—1 Simonton Rd., Camden, Maine. Garden geraniums, ivy geraniums, scented-leaved species.

North Street Greenhouses—Danielson, Conn. Rare species, tuberous-rooted, scented-leaved, selected other types.

Pearce, Rex. D.—Moorestown, New Jersey. Selected list, all types.

Pelargonium Farm—Rte. 4, Box 370, Escondido, Calif. Large selection all types, especially species and scented-leaved.

Rocknoll Nursery—Morrow, Ohio. Occasional rare species.

Schmidt, William E.—355 Lambert Ave., Palo Alto, Calif. All types—does not ship.

Szody's Garden Shop Nursery—1629 Hopkins, Berkeley 6, Calif. Mostly *P. domesticum.*

Thompson's—4342 Wawona St., Los Angeles 41, Calif. *P. hortorum* and *domesticum.*

Terry's Pelargonium Gardens—2597 Crest Drive, Carlsbad, Calif. All types.

Sparks, Myrtle—1108 State St., Bedford, Iowa.

Wagner, Mrs. I. C.—5 Morgan Ave., Norwalk, Conn. Colored leaved *P. hortorum* varieties.

Warren's Nursery—Berkeley 2, Calif. *P. hortorum, domesticum,* and a few *peltatum.*

Wilson Brothers—Roachdale, Indiana. Garden geraniums, fancy leaved, ivy geraniums.

Lingruen, Robert—273 Lintner Ave., Gahanna, Ohio. Specialist in colored leaved varieties.